ROMEO &
JULIET

Cover Design by Nancy Peach

High Noon Books
A division of Academic Therapy Publications
20 Commercial Boulevard
Novato, CA 94949-6191

International Standard Book Number: 1-57128-124-X

9 8 7 6 5 4 3 2 1 0
1 0 9 8 7 6 5 4 3 2

Table of Contents

ABOUT
WILLIAM SHAKESPEARE
(1564-1616)

William Shakespeare was born in Stratford-on-Avon, a market town about eighty miles northwest of London. His father was a glovemaker and a trader in wool, hides, and grain. The family, which had eight children, while not rich, led a comfortable life. William was the third child in the family, and it is thought that he attended the Stratford grammar school where classes started at six or seven in the morning and lasted until five or six in the late afternoon. When the family's finances declined, it became necessary for him to leave school to go to work for a local tradesman.

He married Anne Hathaway when he was eighteen and she was twenty-six. They had three children, including twins.

It is not known exactly when or why Shakespeare left Stratford and moved to London where he quickly became involved in the theater both as an actor and a playwright. Theaters in London were closed from 1592 to 1594 because of the terrifying plague that swept throughout Europe, so Shakespeare spent his time writing plays and publishing two long narrative poems that immediately became popular and started him on the road to fame.

We can tell from the records of the number of properties he bought in London and Stratford that his income was more than ample. His days were busy acting at the Blackfriar and Globe Theaters and writing new plays to be performed there.

Shakespeare was only 52 when he died in Stratford. His birthplace and Anne Hathaway's cottage have been furnished to look as much as possible as they did in Shakespeare's time and are visited by thousands of tourists and admirers each year.

To this day Shakespeare's works can be found on stages in every country in the world. The work of no other playwright has been performed in so many nations throughout so many centuries. His friend Ben Johnson wrote in 1623, "He was not of an age, but for all of time." By now we know Johnson's observation was absolutely correct!

Romeo & Juliet

The Story

Part I

There is a story that I would like to tell you. It is a story of happiness and tragedy. It is the story of great hatred and great love. And it is a story of revenge and forgiveness. Although these events happened more than four hundred years ago, it is still an important story today. It has been told and retold many times in many ways. In fact, this story may well be one of the most popular stories of all time.

This story took place in the city of Verona that is in the country of Italy. In this city there lived two wealthy families. They were constantly fighting with each other. One family had the name Montague. The other family had the name Capulet. These two families had hated each other for so long that no one could even remember why they disliked one another. Each family taught their children from birth to hate the other family. The children never asked why. No one ever asked that question. If they had, there would be no answer. It was hatred without reason. It was as simple as that. And as foolish as that.

Our story begins when two servants from the Capulet house, Samson and Gregory, were walking down the street. They met two servants from the Montague house, Abraham and Balthasar. The two Capulet servants decided to start a fight with the Montague servants. This is how bitter the feelings were between the two families. Even the servants wanted to get into the act. Did they think fighting would please their masters? Or did they just not think?

They knew they had to be careful about starting these fights. The Prince of Verona did not allow fighting in the streets. He had strict punishments for those who broke this law. The Capulet servants did not want to get in trouble with the police. They decided to give the Montague servants dirty looks as they passed. Then they insulted them with an obscene thumb gesture.

"Hey, you," said Abraham, one of the Montague servants. "Did you just do what I thought you did?" He was referring to the gesture.

"I sure did," answered Samson. "But I didn't mean it for you. Now, what are you going to do about it?"

"If you're looking for a fight, you're going to get it," said Abraham as he drew his sword.

The Capulet servants were pleased that the Montague servant pulled his sword first. Now they could tell the police they had fought in self-defense. They both quickly pulled their swords. The four servants began to fight. Luckily, before anyone got hurt, a nephew of the Montague family, Benvolio, came by. He stopped the fight.

"Break it up, you fools," shouted Benvolio. "You don't know what you're doing!" For a moment it looked as if there would be no more fighting. That probably would have been the end of it if someone else had not come by. That someone was Tybalt, a nephew of the Capulet family. He just happened to be coming down the street when he saw the fight. He drew his sword immediately. Tybalt never turned down a chance for a good fight.

"Get ready to die, Benvolio!" said Tybalt. His voice was filled with rage.

"Tybalt, get ahold of yourself. Can't you see that I'm just trying to stop this fight between our servants? I don't want to fight. I want peace. Put your sword away," said Benvolio.

"What makes you think that I want peace? I hate that word almost as much as I hate the Montagues!" said Tybalt. "Come on, coward. Fight like a man."

Benvolio had no choice. He had to draw his sword to defend himself. He was an excellent swordsman. As they fought, a crowd started to gather around them. The people of Verona didn't like fighting in their streets. It was dangerous to have sword fights right in the middle of town. They were also disgusted with the feud between these two families. They had seen too much of their anger through the years. Pretty soon, the crowd started to chant, "Down with the Capulets! Down with the Montagues!"

As the crowd chanted, two well-dressed people turned the corner. It was Lord and Lady Capulet. "What's going on here?" asked Lord Capulet. "Give me my sword." He apparently wanted to join the fighting.

"You old fool. You would have more use for a crutch than a sword," answered his wife.

Just at that moment, Lord and Lady Montague came upon the street scene. "I need my sword now!" said Lord Capulet. "Don't you see old Montague will kill me if I can't defend myself."

"There's my worst enemy," said Montague as he saw Capulet. "Let me at him!" He headed toward Capulet as if to attack, but his wife grabbed him.

"Don't you even think about getting into that fight," Lady Capulet ordered.

Just then the Prince of Verona came upon the crowd in the street. He had heard the commotion and wanted to see what was going on. When he turned the corner and found these two families, he became very angry. In a loud growl, he shouted, "You are not men! You are animals.

You will not be satisfied until you kill your neighbors. Throw down those bloody weapons this instant!"

Everybody in the fight threw their swords quickly to the ground. They knew that their prince was furious. They didn't want to make him more angry. He continued to shout, "Listen to me and listen well. I have caught you fighting in the streets three times now. Three times you have disturbed the peace of Verona. Three times you have endangered the lives of our citizens. You don't care about anything except for your old feud. You Montagues and Capulets are hateful people. Your fight is so old. You don't even know what you are fighting about. We are all sick of your hatred! If you ever again disturb the peaceful streets of Verona, you will pay for it with your lives! Do you understand? Everybody get out of here NOW!"

Everyone quickly left the scene. The Montagues walked home with their nephew, Benvolio. As they walked, they asked him about the fight. Lord Montague wanted to know who had started it. Benvolio explained that he was only trying to stop the servants from fighting. Lady Montague said that she was glad that Romeo, her son, wasn't involved in the fight. "By the way have you seen him?" she asked Benvolio.

Benvolio told them that he had seen Romeo walking in the woods early that morning. He seemed very sad and wouldn't even talk to him. "What's wrong with him?" asked Benvolio.

"We don't know," answered Montague. "He shuts himself up in his room all day long. He closes the curtains and lights a candle. Sometimes when he comes out, it looks as if he has been crying."

"We are really worried about him," said Lady Montague.

Benvolio told his uncle and aunt that he would try to

find out what was troubling his cousin. He left the Montagues and went on to find Romeo.

Romeo Montague was a handsome young man. It could be said that he was probably the most handsome man in all of Verona. He was also charming and sensitive. Romeo thought deeply about everything. When people saw him in the streets, he would often forget to return their greeting. Some people thought that he was a snob. That wasn't true. He was usually thinking so deeply about something that he didn't even hear or see people. Sometimes he was depressed for no special reason.

Romeo's deep thoughts were often about love. He liked to write love letters and poetry about his feelings. In this way, he was a bit different from most boys of that time. Most of his friends seldom thought about romance. They were more interested in sword fighting or horseback riding. In truth, Romeo's friends thought he was a little strange.

Later Benvolio came across Romeo sitting under a tree on the edge of town. "Romeo, it's good to see you. Your parents told me that you were feeling depressed lately. I wondered if you would like to talk about it," said Benvolio.

"There's nothing to be gained from talking about it. There's nothing you can do. I'm in love with someone who doesn't love me. It's as simple as that. I feel so miserable, I wish I were dead," said Romeo with a deep sigh.

"You can't mean that, Romeo. Just who is this woman? And why do you think she is so wonderful?" asked Benvolio.

"Her name is Rosaline," said Romeo. "The beautiful Rosaline who has no interest in me."

"Listen to me," said Benvolio. "There are plenty of other women out there. The only way to get over one woman is to replace her with another. That's my best advice. Now cheer up, Sport. There are better days ahead for you."

At that time, a servant came up to Romeo and Benvolio. "Excuse me, men," he said. "Can either of you read?"

"Of course, what do you need?" answered Romeo. The servant looked relieved. He explained that his master had asked him to invite the guests for a big party that night. He had given the servant the guest list. The servant was too embarrassed to tell his master that he couldn't read it. Romeo and Benvolio read the invitation and the guest list to the servant. Romeo started to get curious about the party. He asked, "Who is having this fancy party?"

"My master, Lord Capulet. Why don't you come, too? Anyone who is not a Montague is invited," said the servant. Romeo and Benvolio gave each other knowing looks. Wouldn't the servant have been surprised if he knew that he was speaking to Montagues! The servant ran off. He was way behind schedule with the invitations.

"Did you hear that, Romeo? A party at the Capulets. You know that Rosaline will be there. This is another chance for you," said Benvolio. He was convinced that this party was just what Romeo needed. He suggested that they wear masks so that the Capulets would not know them. At that time it was stylish for young men to go to parties wearing masks.

At first Romeo was reluctant. Then Benvolio offered him a challenge. "Listen to me, Romeo. Go to the party. When you see all of those beautiful young girls at the party, you will have second thoughts about Rosaline. Compare her face to the other beauties of Verona. She'll look like a crow."

"You are crazy," answered Romeo. "There is no one under the sun who is as beautiful as Rosaline. You'll see what I mean if we go to the party. You will eat those words."

"I doubt it," said Benvolio. "You'll see what a mistake you've made when you see her sitting next to the real beauties of Verona!"

"That settles it. I'll go. I'll go just to prove you wrong!" said Romeo.

Meanwhile at the Capulet house, another young person was thinking about the party. Young Juliet, the only daughter of the Capulets, had been called to her mother's bedroom. Juliet was a lovely girl who was not quite fourteen. She was a kind and gentle child. Juliet was looking forward to the party. She was already dressed for it. Her dress was a gorgeous shade of blue with silver threads running through it. Her dark hair was tied back with silver ribbons. She was a vision of loveliness. When she came into her mother's bedroom, she also found her nanny there.

"Juliet, I have something I want to talk to you about. Would you like to be married?" asked Lady Capulet.

"Married?" said a very surprised Juliet. She could hardly believe her mother's words. She had been thinking of all the different men that she might dance with at the party that night. Her mother's question was quite unexpected. She wasn't sure how to answer. "Well, it is something that I dream of . . . for the future."

"I want you to think about it now. There are many married girls in Verona your age. Some already have children. As a matter of fact, when I was your age I had already given birth to you," explained Lady Capulet.

"She's right, Juliet. You should be thinking about becoming a wife," Nanny added. She always had lots of advice for everyone.

"There is a young man whose name is Paris. He has approached us about winning your hand," Mrs. Capulet said.

"Now he is a catch! What a fine young man he is," said Nanny.

"What do you think, my dear? Do you think you could love this man? Would you have him for your husband?" asked Lady Capulet.

"I don't know, Mother. I could certainly meet him and then tell you what I think. I could try to care for him," answered the obedient daughter.

"Very well, my dear. He will be at the party. Take a good look. I think you will like what you see. He really is a fine young man," said Lady Capulet. She was certain that when her daughter saw how handsome Paris was, she would agree to marry him. Juliet had always been such a joy to her parents. She would not disappoint them now.

The servant then called them to dinner. The party had begun. Juliet and her mother joined the gala.

Romeo, Mercutio, Benvolio, and several of their friends walked together to the Capulet party. All of these young men wore masks.

"Should we make some kind of excuse for wearing masks to the party?" asked Romeo.

"What could we say? It's not any special event that calls for a mask. Let them think what they will. We'll be gone soon so it doesn't really matter," answered Benvolio.

Although they were all dressed and masked for the party, Romeo was feeling depressed. "Let me be the one to carry the torch. I'm feeling sad tonight. I'll just hold the light," he suggested.

"Absolutely not! We want you to be the one

dancing," said Mercutio emphatically.

"Not I," replied Romeo. I am too sad to dance tonight. My unhappiness weighs me down like lead. You dance."

"But you are the one who is in love. You should be walking on air!" argued Mercutio.

"Is that really how love is supposed to make you feel? I feel as if I have been stabbed with Cupid's arrow. All I feel is pain," said Romeo.

"If you feel like that, you have to fight back," said Mercutio. He was determined to get Romeo out of his sad mood. "If love stabs you with a knife, get a knife and stab it back. Tonight our faces are hidden so we may do as we like!"

"Come on, you two. Let's knock and go in. As soon as we get in, it's every man for himself," said Benvolio.

"Give me the torch. I'm done with the game of love. I was never any good at it," said Romeo. He was resisting his friends' efforts to have fun.

His friends continued to tease him. They encouraged him to look forward to the evening. Romeo still couldn't shake his gloomy feeling. "I'm afraid. I have this feeling that something terrible is going to happen to me. Something that will cause my death." His friends weren't listening to his words. They were already knocking on the door of the party.

Lord Capulet was a gracious host. He happily greeted his guests at the door. He was pleased to see the young masked men. He said, "Welcome to the party. There are many beautiful women here who will dance with you. Why, I remember when I was a young man. I used to wear a mask to parties. I've whispered my share of stories to beautiful women while wearing a mask. Have a good time tonight!"

The ballroom was beautifully decorated. There was

lovely music, fine foods, and the best wine. It was one of the most extravagant parties that Verona had ever seen. After dinner, Lord Capulet announced that the dancing should begin. Soon the young ladies started whirling around the ballroom floor in the arms of handsome young men. The dance floor was filled with beauty and grace. The brilliant gowns that the ladies wore looked like giant fans opening and closing as their partners guided them to the sounds of the music. It was a very romantic evening.

Romeo had been watching Juliet with interest as she danced with another young man. At first, he had just glanced her way. He was actually looking for his beautiful Rosaline. Then he found that his eyes could not leave Juliet. "What a gorgeous young woman she is," he said to himself.

As Romeo watched Juliet more, he felt as if he were in a trance. He was hypnotized by her beauty. "I guess Benvolio was right. I did not know what true beauty was until tonight," sighed Romeo. He had to find out who she was. He stopped a servant who was carrying a large tray of grapes to the table. "Tell me, please," Romeo said, "who is that enchanting woman?" He pointed to Juliet.

No sooner had the words left Romeo's lips than Tybalt recognized the voice. "That's the voice of a Montague! There's no mistaking it. He is here in this house. The house of Capulet!" Tybalt told his servant to get his sword. He ran to tell his uncle. "Uncle, there is a Montague right here in your house tonight. Your worst enemy has come to ruin your party," said Tybalt.

"Is it Romeo, by any chance?" asked Lord Capulet. He did not seem upset by the news.

"Yes, it is that scum, Romeo," answered Tybalt.

"Tybalt let him alone. He is behaving like a

gentleman. The truth is that he is a well-respected young man of Verona. I would not treat him poorly in my house. Not for all the money in town. I want you to be patient and ignore him. Do you understand? Now stop that scowling and frowning. You are the one who's going to ruin the party," said Capulet in a stern voice.

"Uncle, I can't bear it. To have our worst enemy in the house, here at your party!" argued Tybalt.

"Now listen here. This is my house. You will do what you are told under my roof," ordered Capulet in a way that Tybalt could not ignore.

"But it is such a shame," said Tybalt in a last effort to get his uncle to change his mind.

"Go now. I don't want to hear any more of this," insisted Capulet. Tybalt had no choice but to do as he was told. He didn't like it. Not one bit.

"This is unbelievable. How can Uncle put up with this? I'll be patient now. Later I'll have my opportunity to get even with Romeo," Tybalt whispered to himself. He was trembling with rage. Tybalt was always angry about something. It was as if he could not be satisfied unless there was a reason to be angry. He couldn't believe his eyes when he saw Romeo approach his cousin Juliet.

Romeo asked Juliet for a dance. They moved to the dance floor and joined the other couples. As soon as they began dancing, both of them felt a magic they had not felt before. They gazed into each other's eyes. Although it was the first time, they felt as if they knew each other well. Romeo could not help himself. He pulled her near to him and kissed her lips. Juliet did not resist. The moment was broken by Nanny, who tugged at Juliet's sleeve. She said, "Your mother wants a word with you." Juliet separated unwillingly from her partner. She left the dance floor, but her eyes stayed on Romeo.

"Who is her mother?" Romeo asked Nanny.

"Her mother is Lady Capulet, the lady of the house," she said as she turned and ran after Juliet.

Romeo could not believe what he had heard. How could he have such terrible luck? To have fallen in love with a Capulet! It couldn't be true. It simply could not be true. But, alas, it was! Fate had played a terrible trick on these young people.

When Juliet's nanny caught up with her, Juliet had a question. "Nanny, do you know who that young man was? The one I was dancing with?"

"No, I don't know who he is," answered Nanny.

"Please, run and find out before he leaves. I have to know. If he's married, I'll just die," said Juliet.

Her nanny returned with the bad news. He might as well have been married. He was a Montague. "His name is Romeo. He is the son of your father's worst enemy," said Nanny, who was out of breath from running.

"How can this be?" cried Juliet. "How can the love of my life come from the family that I hate? This doesn't seem possible. I'm doomed to love a hated enemy."

"Come, Juliet," answered Nanny. "It's time for bed. The guests are all leaving."

The party was coming to an end. Lord Capulet was saying goodbye to all of his guests. The musicians were putting away their instruments. The food was being cleared from the tables. What a party! It was hard to imagine that this festive evening would be the cause of a tragic chain of events.

Part II

Romeo could not stay away from Juliet. After the party he climbed over the wall around the Capulet house to look for her. He was nervous. He did not want to be caught sneaking around in the dark there. Yet he felt desperate to find Juliet. Then he caught a glimpse of her on the balcony. He moved closer to where she stood. He couldn't believe his good fortune! She was actually standing on the balcony alone.

He couldn't believe his ears when he heard her words, "Romeo, Romeo, wherefore art thou, Romeo? If only you would love me. I would give up my father and my name." Of course, Juliet had no idea that Romeo was standing right under her balcony. He was listening to every word she said.

Romeo didn't know what to do. He felt as if he were in a very awkward situation. Should he let her know that he was there? Or should he be quiet and try to hear more of her feelings?

Juliet spoke again. "It is only the Montague name that is my enemy. It is not the person who is the enemy. What is in a name anyhow? If a rose weren't called a rose, it would still smell as sweet. And my Romeo would still be perfection if he were called by another name. His name is not part of the person he is. Oh, Romeo, if you could only get rid of that name!"

At that point, Romeo could no longer keep still. "I will hold you to your word. I'll get rid of my name. I'll

21

even be baptized with a new name if you will love me," he called to her.

The unexpected sound of Romeo's voice frightened Juliet. It made her jump. "Who is out there? Tell me or I will call my father's guards," she cried.

"I don't know what name to tell you. I hate my real name because it is an enemy to you," answered Romeo.

"I know who you are. Just from those few words. Is it you, Romeo, the Montague?" Juliet asked.

"I can't be Romeo or a Montague if you dislike those names," said Romeo.

"I cannot believe you found me! These orchard walls are high. The grounds are carefully guarded at night. How did you find your way to me?" asked Juliet. She was very surprised that Romeo could end up at her balcony. She was also worried for his safety. "Do you know that if my family finds you here, you will be murdered?"

"If you love me, Juliet, I don't care if they murder me. I would rather have your love for a few moments and die than to live without your love," answered Romeo.

"How did you know which direction to go to find me?" Juliet asked.

"Love directed me to you. The power of love was all I needed. It brought me to you," said Romeo. He continued to tell Juliet how he felt. The words of love flowed as if they had been held back for a very long time. And yet, that could not have been the case. He had only known Juliet for a few short hours.

"Do you really love me? Do you swear it?" asked Juliet.

"I swear my love for you by the moon," answered Romeo.

"Don't swear by the moon. The orbit of the moon is always changing. Swear by something that is constant. Something that does not change. Oh, never mind. Don't swear at all. I'm afraid that our feelings of love have come about too suddenly. Maybe we will feel differently tomorrow. Let's just see what happens. We'll say good night for now. Let's hope that our love is like a rosebud that will bloom into a gorgeous flower when we meet tomorrow," said Juliet.

"Juliet, please don't leave me like this tonight," begged Romeo.

"What do you want?" asked Juliet.

"I want you to swear to be faithful to me," he said.

"I gave you my vow of love. You heard it," she answered.

Just then a voice from inside called for Juliet. It was Nanny. "I'll be right back. Wait for me," Juliet said. When she returned, she said, "Romeo, you must tell me the truth. Is this a game you are playing with my heart? Or do you love me truly? If this is not a game, then you must propose marriage. If you are sincere, return tomorrow and tell me what arrangements you have made for our wedding. Return with word by nine o'clock so I can make plans."

Juliet's words were music to Romeo's ears. She would not have spoken of marriage if she did not love him. He promised to return to her tomorrow with details for a wedding. Romeo blew a kiss to her. He left to climb the orchard walls. He heard her sweet voice whisper as he made his way to the orchard wall. "Good night, good night. Parting is such sweet sorrow that I shall say good night till it be morrow." Romeo loved everything Juliet said, but he especially treasured these words as he ran off into the cool damp night.

As soon as Romeo left the Capulet grounds, he rushed off to find the priest. Friar Lawrence had been a close family friend since his childhood days. Romeo was certain that the Friar would help him. He was so excited when he found Friar Lawrence. He forgot to tell him that he had a new love. Friar Lawrence thought that Romeo was talking about Rosaline, his old love. He was shocked to learn that someone new had taken Rosaline's place.

He scolded Romeo for falling in love again so soon. "Didn't you just tell me that Rosaline was the love of your life? How can you change your feelings like that? Don't answer that. I'll tell you how. Young men love with their eyes – not their hearts. Good grief, boy, think of all those tears you wasted over Rosaline," he said, shaking his head.

"Father, you always scolded me for loving Rosaline," said Romeo.

"Make no mistake, Romeo. I scolded you for being infatuated with her. I never thought you really loved her," said the Friar.

"You told me to get over her," said Romeo.

"That's true, but I didn't tell you to fall head over heels with another. You love Rosaline one day and Juliet the next? How can that be?" asked Friar Lawrence.

Friar Lawrence was very reluctant to agree to perform this wedding. He knew the families would be furious when they found out. Yet the Friar was also a wise old man. He knew that Romeo and Juliet would find some other way of marrying if he refused. He was worried that they would run off and never be heard from again. Friar Lawrence had an idea. He thought that perhaps this union might stop the bitter feuding between the families.

"Please don't lecture me anymore," begged Romeo. "All I know is that I love Juliet now. I must have her for my wife."

"Very well, my son. I'll marry you," said the Friar.

"Let's hurry and perform the ceremony as soon as possible," said Romeo.

The old Friar shook his head. "Those who are in a hurry often stumble and fall. It's better to move slowly and wisely." Romeo was not listening to these words. He was thinking only of Juliet.

While Romeo was with the Friar, Mercutio and Benvolio had been looking for him. Benvolio had been to Romeo's house to see if he could find him there. Lord Montague had told Benvolio that Tybalt had sent a letter challenging Romeo to a duel. He felt certain that Romeo would want to fight Tybalt.

"Poor Romeo," said Mercutio. "He's already been killed by love."

At that same time Romeo walked by. Mercutio and Benvolio teased him about slipping out of the party last night. Romeo told his friends that he had to do something of great importance. They couldn't help but notice that he was no longer in his gloomy mood. When they asked him about his change, Romeo just smiled. He couldn't tell them his secret. They would soon know.

Juliet's nanny and a Capulet servant were looking for Romeo. They came upon him talking with his cousin and friend. Nanny asked the young men if they knew Romeo. Mercutio and Benvolio started making fun of the old woman. They teased Romeo that this old woman was his new love. The nanny became very upset because the young men were disrespectful.

Nanny asked to speak to Romeo in private. She told him that Juliet was waiting to hear word about their marriage. Romeo explained the arrangements. He told her to bring Juliet to Friar Lawrence's monastery that afternoon for the wedding. He offered her money, but the old lady refused. Romeo offered a second time, and she grabbed the money. She left quickly to give Juliet the good news.

Meanwhile, Juliet was frantic. The nanny had

promised to return in half an hour with news from Romeo. Three hours later, she had still not come back. What could be the cause of such a delay? "Why is she taking so long! Old people are so slow. Their feet move like lead," said Juliet with exasperation. Finally she heard Nanny's footsteps.

It was difficult to get the story from Nanny. She kept talking about some rude men who had been with Romeo. Finally Nanny told her what she wanted to hear. Romeo had arranged for the wedding to take place. They were to meet in Friar Lawrence's room and go to the church together. Juliet quickly left home to meet her groom. This was a dream come true.

The wedding ceremony was short and sweet. To the young lovers, it was a perfect celebration. They did not care that there could be no fine wedding clothes. They did not care that there were no beautiful flowers at the altar. No music from the organ. No family or friends to give congratulations. They knew only that this ceremony united them forever. From this day on no one could separate them. At least this is what they thought as they stood before Friar Lawrence on their wedding day.

They made plans for Romeo to come to Juliet's room that night. At that time they would decide how to announce their marriage to their families. They knew that the news would have to be given at the right time. They weren't quite sure how to do this. They were certain of only one thing. They had found true love with one another. True love whose bonds could never be broken. As they said goodbye at the church, they were enjoying the happiest moment of their young lives.

Part III

As Romeo walked through the streets of Verona, he saw everything a little bit differently. He noticed trees he had never noticed before. He saw the vivid colors of flowers that he had not seen before. People seemed friendlier. The sky seemed to be bluer. For the first time in a long time, everything seemed perfect. That perfect feeling was to be short lived. As Romeo turned a corner near the center of town, his destiny was to be forever changed.

At this crossroad he found Benvolio and Mercutio. They were speaking in unfriendly terms to Tybalt and his friend, Petruchio.

"There is my man now," said Tybalt. His voice was accusatory. He pointed as if he had been waiting for him. "You are a villain, Romeo."

Romeo had no interest in quarreling with Tybalt. He knew that Juliet cared deeply for her cousin. Now Juliet was his wife. That also made Tybalt his family. "Tybalt, I am not a villain. You don't know anything about me," said Romeo.

Tybalt answered, "Listen here, boy. Draw your sword and fight. You have to pay for what you have done!" Tybalt was referring to Romeo's uninvited visit to the Capulet party.

"I don't know what you are talking about. I haven't done anything to you. And I'm not going to fight you. I respect the Capulet name as I do my own," said Romeo.

At that time Mercutio got into the fight. He couldn't stand listening to Romeo say that he respected the Capulet name. "What are you talking about? What a cowardly thing to say, Romeo. Come on, Tybalt. I'll fight you," said Mercutio.

Tybalt and Mercutio began fighting. They traded insults with one another. They fought on as Romeo begged them to stop. Finally, Romeo couldn't stand it any longer. He was afraid that someone was going to get seriously injured. He yelled out, "Don't you remember what the prince told us? Stop it both of you!"

At that minute Romeo placed himself between the two fighters. His intent was to stop the fighting. Unfortunately, Romeo's movement put Mercutio in a spot where he could not defend himself for a moment. In that brief time, Tybalt put his sword into Mercutio.

Mercutio cried out, "I am hurt. Get me a doctor."

"Is it bad?" asked Romeo in a worried voice.

"Romeo, why did you do that?" asked Mercutio as he bled. "You gave him the chance to wound me."

"I didn't mean it. I just wanted you to stop fighting. I'm so sorry. I thought I was doing the right thing," said Romeo. He was sick with guilt. Had he caused Mercutio's wound?

"Get me out of the street. I'm bleeding to death. I'm afraid I'm going to die." Those were to be Mercutio's last words.

"He's dead! He's dead!" cried Benvolio as he held Mercutio in his arms.

"What have I done?" cried Romeo. "My love for Juliet made me weak. I acted like a woman when I should have acted like a man. Now my good friend is dead, and it's all because of me." At that moment Tybalt returned to the scene. He was again ready to fight. Even though he knew he had killed Mercutio, he wanted more Montague blood.

This time Romeo was ready to fight.

The fight was short. Romeo's anger and hurt made him strong in battle. He soon struck Tybalt with his sword. Tybalt fell to the ground. Benvolio walked over to him. "He is dead, Romeo. Quick! You must run for your life. The Prince will surely sentence you to death if he finds you," said Benvolio.

Romeo knew that Benvolio was right. But his sad heart made his feet heavy. How could this be his destiny? He realized he was about to lose everything he cared for. He could not move.

"What are you waiting for? Leave now or lose your life!" cried Benvolio.

Romeo turned and ran.

Moments later a police officer came to the scene. Soon the Prince arrived. Then came the Capulets followed by the Montagues. They had been told that their families had once again been involved in bloodshed. Benvolio told the story of the fighting. He tried carefully to explain how Romeo had tried to keep out of it until his friend Mercutio had been killed.

The Capulets argued that he should not be believed because he was a member of the Montague family. The Montagues begged for mercy for their son. The Capulets demanded that Romeo be put to death for Tybalt's murder.

The Prince spoke. "Romeo, must be exiled. There can be no other answer. He took another life. I told both families that I would not tolerate this fighting in Verona. Your families chose not to listen to my orders. If Romeo ever comes back, he will be put to death. That is all I have to say. Except that I hope you are all satisfied," he said with disgust in his voice.

Lord Montague hung his head while Lady Montague wept quietly. Lord Capulet felt sadness for the loss of his nephew. He knew that Tybalt was a hothead. In his heart he knew that Tybalt probably was at fault for the fight. But he could not have said that. It would have been disloyal to his family. Lady Capulet wept loudly. Tybalt was her brother's only son. He would be missed dearly. Misery hung like a dark cloud over the Montagues and the Capulets as they slowly walked to their homes. Once again, the feud had caused pain and grief to both families.

Meanwhile, Juliet was unaware of all that had taken place. She sat in her bedroom at her mirror. She brushed her hair and dreamed of the evening to come. She could not wait to see her Romeo again. She hummed softly to herself as she thought about her wedding night. Juliet went through her closet again. She had changed dresses three times so far. She wanted to be wearing something that would be perfect.

Juliet was jarred from her daydreams of Romeo by her nanny's heavy rushing footsteps up the stairs and into her room. Nanny's face was pale as she barged into the room. "He is dead! He is dead! I cannot believe my eyes and ears. He is dead!" She clutched at Juliet and fell trembling into her arms.

Now Juliet's face lost all color. For a brief moment, she looked as if she would faint. The shock was so great for her. Her eyes turned dull. In a low voice she said, "Tell me what has happened to my Romeo. Tell me the whole story."

"I can hardly believe it myself. It's too awful to tell," said Nanny.

"You must tell me," begged Juliet. "Did Romeo take poison and kill himself? If he did, I will kill myself, too. Or did someone kill him? Tell me everything."

Juliet's nanny was crying and carrying on loudly. She was paying little attention to Juliet's face and expression. She didn't realize what Juliet was saying. Nanny was, in fact, reporting the death of Tybalt. She was so wrapped up in this story that she failed to see that she was creating a misunderstanding. "I saw the wound myself. It was deep and bloody. I saw him lying in the street. It was a horrible sight," cried Nanny.

"Oh my God! My dearest Romeo is dead. My heart will surely break into pieces!" cried Juliet.

"You're right. Tybalt was such a dear gentleman. He was always so kind to me. What a pity he is dead now," said Nanny.

Juliet looked up from her tears. "Why are you talking about Tybalt? You said Romeo was dead."

Nanny gave Juliet a blank look. "Oh, no. Romeo is not dead. He has been banished by the Prince. He has to leave Verona at once and can never return."

"But why, Nanny? Is Romeo banished because he is the one who killed Tybalt?" asked Juliet.

Nanny began to tell her the story of the fight. Juliet was heartbroken. She cried loudly. She threw herself on her bed. She pounded the pillows with all her might. Nanny thought that she was crying for her dead cousin. She was really crying for her lost husband. It was not that she didn't love Tybalt. She did. Yet she loved her husband more. She also knew that Tybalt had a terrible temper and was always looking for trouble. If Romeo killed Tybalt, Juliet was certain that he did so in self-defense. She didn't need to hear any more of the story.

Juliet could hardly believe that Nanny had told the truth. How could her husband have killed her dearest cousin? How could it be possible that her wedding day was also the day that her husband would be sent into exile? It was like being married and divorced on the same day.

Juliet begged Nanny to find Romeo. She wanted to

see him one last time before he left the city. "Please, Nanny, find my Romeo and give him this wedding ring. Tell him to come to me and say his farewell." Then Juliet started to cry again. The nanny knew that Romeo was hiding in Friar Lawrence's room at the monastery. She ran to get him for Juliet. Nanny couldn't stand to see her so unhappy.

Romeo had been waiting in Friar Lawrence's room for the priest to return. Friar Lawrence had gone into town to find out about Romeo's punishment. When he returned, he told Romeo that the Prince had ruled that he be exiled. "You are never to return to Verona. From this day on you must live outside the walls of this city," said the Friar sadly.

Romeo was torn apart with sadness. He told the Friar, "I would rather be dead than banished."

"Romeo, the world out there is very wide. Be patient. You will find a place for yourself," replied Friar Lawrence as gently as he could. He knew the depth of grief with which this young man was struggling.

"Father, there is no world for me outside the walls of Verona. My Juliet lives here in this city. Heaven is where she lives. Hell is everywhere else." With those words, Romeo wept. He was sick at heart.

"My dear boy, I know it must seem like that today. But the truth is that death is a far worse punishment than exile," the Friar said.

At that moment there was a gentle knock on the door. Friar Lawrence opened the door to find Juliet's nanny. "Please, sir, tell me where I may find Juliet's husband," begged Nanny.

"At the moment he is drowning in his own tears," replied Friar Lawrence.

"Oh my," Nanny said. "He is in the same state as Juliet. She just lies on her bed weeping and crying out.

She is beside herself. Romeo, I have a message from your wife."

"Please tell me what she says. Does she no longer love me?" cried Romeo.

"She cries for her cousin, and she cries for her husband. The dear child's heart is broken," said the nanny. "Every time she tries to get up, she falls down and begins weeping again."

"If she no longer loves me, I will no longer live," cried Romeo. As he said these words, he held a dagger to his breast.

Friar Lawrence grabbed the knife from Romeo's hand. "Are you a man?" he yelled at Romeo. "If you are, act like one. For goodness' sake, you cry like a woman, and you act like an animal. Pull yourself together, boy."

Then Friar Lawrence began to tell Romeo all the reasons he had to be happy. He pointed out that if he had not killed Tybalt, Tybalt would have killed him. He reminded him that the Prince could have sentenced him to death, but, instead, his life was spared.

"You also have the love of a beautiful woman. You have all these reasons to be happy and yet you cry like a child. You should be comforting your wife. Go to her room and spend the little time you have left in Verona with Juliet," said the Friar. He promised Romeo that time would heal all wounds. He assured him that he would help to win a pardon for him from the Prince. And that one day he could return to his wife and his family. The Friar told Nanny to return home and tell Juliet that Romeo was on his way to her.

"I'll go at once. Before I do, I must give Romeo the wedding ring that Juliet sent. Come quickly, Romeo. It is getting late," said Nanny in a worried voice.

Romeo was starting to feel more hopeful. "Maybe there is reason to believe in the future."

"Of course, there is," said the Friar. "Remember you must leave Juliet before the break of day. If you don't, the police will catch you. Leave before the break of day and go to Mantua. I will send messages to you and let you know how things stand here. Be patient. Everything will eventually work out." The priest took Romeo's hand to shake it. "Goodbye and good luck to you, Romeo."

As Romeo left to spend his wedding night with his wife, there was more trouble brewing in the Capulet house. At that very moment Lord and Lady Capulet were planning a wedding for Count Paris and Juliet. Lord Capulet had just told Paris that Juliet was too sad about her cousin's death to speak to her about the marriage tonight. However, he promised that he would persuade Juliet to marry Paris. Juliet's father was so confident that he set the wedding for Thursday. That was just three days away. "Is that too soon for you, my son?" Capulet asked Paris.

"Sir, I wish that the wedding was tomorrow," answered Paris.

Capulet told Paris that the wedding would be small. He felt that out of respect for Tybalt, the celebration should be a quiet one. He didn't want people to think that they had forgotten all about Tybalt's death. Capulet told his wife to go talk to Juliet first thing in the morning. He wanted her to get used to the idea of the marriage.

Romeo spent his wedding night with his beloved bride. As the light of the early dawn filtered through Juliet's bedroom window, the couple realized that Romeo would have to leave very soon. A bird sang a melody whose tune drifted through the orchard and up through the window. Romeo got up to leave. Juliet pulled him back. "Romeo, that song you heard was the nightingale. I know the song well. She sits on a tree in the orchard and sings me to sleep each night."

"No, my darling, that was the lark. It was the lark telling us that morning has arrived. And I must go now or die."

"Please, Romeo, stay. The light that you see is the light from the moon. It is not daylight. You don't have to be gone yet," said Juliet.

"If my darling wife says that it is not morning, then it is not morning. And if it is, so be it. I will gladly be caught and killed if Juliet wishes that," said Romeo to his new wife.

With those chilling words, Juliet knew that Romeo must go at once. It was indeed morning. "Go, Romeo. Go now."

Romeo looked out the window. "The lighter it becomes, the darker our troubles become," he sighed.

No sooner had he said those words than Nanny came running into the room. "Juliet, your mother is coming to your bedroom. It's morning!" she said. Her voice sounded worried.

"The day is coming in the window, and my life is going out that same window," said Juliet.

"Farewell, my darling. One kiss and I'll be gone," said Romeo. The departing kiss was short and sweet.

"You must write to me every hour," begged Juliet. "I will count every minute until we are together again."

"I promise I will," whispered Romeo.

"Do you really think that we will see one another again?" asked Juliet.

"I know for sure that we will be together again. Our troubles will fade and there will be sweet times ahead," promised Romeo. With those remarks, he made his way down the ladder that Juliet had made out of cords.

Romeo took one final look up at Juliet. At that moment she was struck with a strange feeling. She felt as if she were looking down into a grave holding her husband. Juliet was deeply troubled by this vision. Her gloomy thoughts were interrupted by her mother who entered the room at that time.

"Daughter," said Lady Capulet, "are you up?"

"Yes, Mother," replied Juliet.

"How are you feeling this morning?"

"Mother, I'm not well at all."

"Are you still mourning the loss of Tybalt? Listen to me, my dear. All your tears can't bring him back from the dead. It's good to show grief. It proves your love of your cousin. But I have to tell you, Juliet, too much grief is foolish. You must get on with your life. That is exactly what I am here to talk to you about. I have some very good news for you," said Lady Capulet.

"I could certainly use some good news at this time," said Juliet. "Please tell me."

"Well, my dear. You have a very kind father who has made plans to cheer you up. He has arranged a special day that will bring you much joy. You are going to be so surprised when I tell you!" said Lady Capulet excitedly.

"Mother, tell me more about this surprise. What special day are you talking about?" asked Juliet.

"This Thursday morning you are to be married at Saint Peter's church to that wonderful young man, Count Paris. Can you imagine?" said Lady Capulet.

Juliet felt as if someone had thrown a pail of icy water on her. The cold slowly seeped through her body until it reached her heart. "How could this be?" she said to herself. To her mother she said, "I will not marry Paris. He has not even come to court me. I'd sooner marry Romeo. And you know how I hate him. What could possibly be the rush?"

Lady Capulet was taken aback when she heard her daughter's reaction. Needless to say, she was very disappointed in Juliet. "Why don't you ask your father?

Here he is now," she answered in a stern voice as Lord Capulet walked through the door.

"Have you told our lovely daughter the good news?" asked Capulet. He had an enormous smile on his face. He was feeling proud because it was a major responsibility for a father to find a good husband for his daughter. And he was overjoyed that he had been able to find such a worthy suitor for Juliet. By all accounts, Paris was considered a catch. Any young woman in Verona would have been thrilled to marry him. Any young woman except his daughter.

"Yes, I have. Do you know what she said?" answered Lady Capulet in a high-pitched loud voice. "She says thanks, but no thanks!"

"What?" said Capulet with disbelief. "Did you say that she is NOT counting her blessings that a young man such as Paris wants to marry her? Are you telling me that she doesn't appreciate her parents' efforts in finding the best husband in all of Verona? Is that what you are telling me?" At that point, Capulet's voice was booming. He was not the type of man who angered quickly or easily. When he did get angry, everybody got out of his way.

In another situation, Juliet would have quickly given in to her father, but how could she? How could she marry when she was already married? Her love for Romeo gave her strength to stand up to her father. In a calm and steady voice she said, "I do thank you, Father, but I don't love him. So I must refuse his offer."

"You are an ungrateful daughter. You are a spoiled brat who should get down on her knees and thank her parents for arranging such a match. Instead you try to tell me that you will not marry? My answer to you is that you will be at the church on Thursday if I have to drag you the whole way. Do you understand?" thundered Capulet.

At her father's words, Juliet sank to her knees and attempted to grab her father's hand. "Please, Father. Please listen to me for just a few words," she softly pleaded.

"You will not speak to me, you disobedient child. I am disgusted with you. Don't you dare say another word to me about this. If you are not at that church on Thursday, you are no longer my daughter." Capulet turned to his wife. "Here we thought we were lucky because we had a child. As it turns out, one child is one too much!"

"Sir, you cannot mean that," interrupted Nanny. It hurt her deeply to have Juliet treated like this. She had been with Juliet ever since she was born. The nanny wanted to protect her.

"Hold your tongue, woman!" shouted Capulet. "Nobody wants to hear a nanny's opinion about this matter."

"Sir, could I just say one thing?" asked Nanny.

"No, you may not. Save it for your gossip sessions with your friends," answered Capulet. He had clearly lost his patience.

"Calm down. You are too angry," said Lady Capulet to her husband.

"I have a right to be angry. I have worked hard all my life to provide for this child. Now finally when I have made her the best match in Verona, she refuses him. Why does this foolish girl refuse him? She says, 'I don't love him. I'm too young. He hasn't courted me.' Well, let me tell you. If you do not marry this man I have chosen for you, you will not live in this house ever again. You will die a beggar in the streets. I will never set eyes on you again. I swear this to you," finished Capulet in a voice overflowing with anger. With these words, he stomped out of Juliet's bedroom.

Juliet turned to her mother. "Mother, please! Mother, help me. Get him to delay the marriage for a week or maybe a month. Please, Mother," she begged.

"You heard your father, Juliet. There is to be no more discussion on this subject." Lady Capulet turned abruptly and left the room with heavy footsteps that resounded down the long hall.

Juliet and her nanny were alone. Juliet put her head in Nanny's lap and asked, "What am I to do? Please help me, Nanny. What am I to do?"

Juliet's nanny was a loving, loyal woman. She had many kind traits, but she was not clever. In fact, she usually did not think things through carefully. She tended to act on her first thoughts. It was not surprising that she said to Juliet, "Here is the situation. Romeo is banished so there's no way that he can do anything about it if you marry Paris. I think you should go ahead and marry him. Nobody will know that you are already married. Paris is handsome and rich. Why, Romeo is a dishrag compared to Paris! You'll be happy if you marry Paris. He's a better match. Your first husband is as good as dead. He's of no use to you."

"Do you really think that is best?" asked Juliet. She was not surprised to hear what Nanny thought of Romeo. She didn't know why she had even bothered to ask her advice.

"You have made me feel much better. Tell my mother that I have gone to Friar Lawrence for confession. I must be forgiven for having displeased my father so," said Juliet.

Nanny quickly moved to get Juliet's coat. She also brought a cloth with warm water to wipe Juliet's tear-swollen face. The nanny felt pleased that everything was going to work out for Juliet.

Part IV

When Juliet arrived at Friar Lawrence's cell, she found her intended husband, Count Paris. He had come to talk with Friar Lawrence about his upcoming wedding to Juliet. Needless to say, the Friar was surprised when he found out that Paris would be marrying Juliet.

Count Paris was pleased to see the young woman he was to marry. "I'm happy to see you, my Juliet and my wife," he said to her.

"That may be true when I am your wife, sir, but not today," answered Juliet. She was annoyed that she had run into him.

"That will be true on Thursday," answered Paris.

"As you say," replied Juliet.

"Did you come here to make a confession to Father Lawrence?" asked Paris. Without waiting for an answer, he added, "Be sure to confess to him that you love me." Paris had no idea that his intended bride was desperately in love with another. He was sure that she was as eagerly awaiting the wedding as he.

"Father, do you have time to hear my confession?" asked Juliet, ignoring Paris.

"Of course, my dear," answered Friar Lawrence.

"I will not disturb your confession, but I must have a kiss before I go," said Paris. He quickly pulled Juliet into his arms and gave her a kiss. "There," he said as if he had given her a great gift. "Keep this kiss until Thursday when there will be many more!"

As soon as he left, the Friar quickly shut the door. He and Juliet began to talk about a solution for her problem. It was obvious that Juliet had not seriously listened to the advice of Nanny. She had no intention of marrying Paris. She told the priest that she would rather jump off the highest tower in Verona than go through with the wedding on Thursday.

The Friar, not wanting Juliet to kill herself and feeling partly to blame for this situation, came up with a plan. This plan was a desperate one. But this was a desperate situation. He told Juliet that if she were brave enough, there was a certain drug that she could take. If she took this drug, it would appear that she was dead. The priest explained that this drug removed all the color from the face. It made the body cold and stiff. If Juliet took this the night before her intended marriage to Paris, he would find her in this state when he came to take her to the church for the wedding.

Friar Lawrence told her that the effects of the drug lasted for forty-two hours. Then the person woke up as if from a pleasant sleep. This time period would be long enough to get Juliet through the funeral. She could then be placed in the family tomb where the Friar promised to watch over her until she woke up.

The Friar's plan was possible because at that time it was not the custom to bury people underground. The bodies of the dead were dressed in their best clothes and carefully placed in a family burial place. This was known as a tomb or vault. Each family had its own vault so that all of the relatives could be together. The bodies were placed on a cement block that resembled a bed. They were left there to disintegrate. The idea of being placed in a family tomb when one was not yet dead, even with the priest's promise to watch over her, was frightening, to say the least.

Friar Lawrence also promised that he would send word to Romeo to come and get her. The couple could then go to Mantua to live as husband and wife. He warned her that she would have to be very brave to follow through with this plan.

Juliet's desperation to be faithful to her husband overruled her fears. "Give me the drug. Don't talk to me about fear. This is the only way," answered Juliet.

Friar Lawrence opened his cabinet and poured the liquid from a large brown bottle into a small green vial. He turned to Juliet. "Here is the drug. I will send word to Romeo in Mantua. I will tell him of our plan. I must leave at once to make these arrangements. Goodbye, Juliet. Be strong."

"Goodbye, dear Father. Thank you for helping me," said Juliet, clutching the green vial in her hands.

As Juliet walked home, her steps were heavy. She felt as if she had the weight of the world on her shoulders. The vial made the palms of her hands sweaty. She was very frightened. Juliet was only thirteen years old and yet she was trying to solve an extremely complicated problem. When she entered her house, she went directly to her father. She told him that she had been to confession to ask forgiveness for being a disobedient daughter. Her father was delighted. Lord Capulet loved his daughter dearly. It would have been a great loss to him to disown her.

He took her in his arms and embraced her. "Go to your room, Juliet. You must prepare for the big event tomorrow. Nanny, go with her. She needs help getting ready for her wedding."

Juliet and Nanny chose the wedding dress from Juliet's closet. Nanny picked the shoes and the jewelry for the dress. She talked as she worked. The nanny chatted about this and that, mostly about what a good match Juliet had made. Nothing was said about Romeo. Juliet was getting very tired. After the clothes and accessories had been set out, she asked Nanny to leave her. "I'm tired tonight. Go see if my mother needs some help with the wedding plans. I'll see you in the morning."

"Goodnight, my child. Sleep tight," said Nanny as she left Juliet.

Juliet slowly began putting on the wedding clothes that would really be her burial clothes. Even though she was tired, she began to worry again. The thought of waking up in the tomb all alone, with all of those bodies, made her very frightened. She was afraid that Tybalt's ghost would come back to haunt her when he found out Romeo was her husband. She was also afraid that the drug in the vial might really be poison. Juliet wondered if Friar Lawrence had given her poison so he would not have to explain his part in this complicated situation. "Maybe he wants me dead because he's afraid that he will get in trouble for marrying Romeo and me without my father's permission," thought Juliet. "How could that be? How could a priest kill someone? That's not likely," she consoled herself with those thoughts.

It suddenly dawned on Juliet that all of those things could be true, but she still had no choice other than to marry Paris. That thought was worse than anything else that she had imagined, including waking up alone among corpses. Juliet loved Romeo more than she valued her own life. That was her last thought as she drank the contents of the vial and fell upon her bed.

As the morning light filtered through Juliet's bedroom, the house was bustling with wedding arrangements. There was a happy feeling throughout the entire house, except for Juliet's room. In this room there was a somber quiet that contrasted to the noise of the rest of the house. Although Juliet slept in her bed, there was no sound of gentle breathing. As the nanny entered the room to wake her, she was surprised to find Juliet sleeping in her wedding clothes.

"What? Did you dress early this morning and then fall back asleep?" she asked. There was no answer. The nanny stepped closer. She started to shake Juliet and then jumped back. She was startled to feel a cold stiff body instead of the warmth she had expected. She put her face down close to Juliet's. There was no breathing. No color in the face. The nanny reacted by screaming at the top of her lungs, "She's dead! She's dead! Juliet is dead!"

Lady Capulet came running into the room. "What are you screaming about? What is going on here?"

"Juliet is dead!" she cried. "What a terrible day!"

"No, this cannot be true. My child, my life! You must be revived or I will die with you. I cannot live without my child," cried Lady Capulet. "Help, help, help!"

At that time Lord Capulet came into the bedroom. "Paris is here for Juliet. Bring her downstairs."

"She's dead! She's dead! What a terrible day!" cried Nanny.

"Let me see her," said the disbelieving Capulet. As he slowly examined her, his face grew pale. He opened her eyelids and looked into her eyes. He picked up her hand and felt the cold. He could not believe what he was seeing. Capulet sat down on the bed, "You are right. she is dead. It's as if death has come like an early frost to kill the sweetest flower in the field." He put his head into his hands and wept.

At that time, Friar Lawrence and Count Paris came through the door. "Is the bride ready to go to the church?" asked Friar Lawrence.

"She's ready to go to the church, but she will never

come back again," answered Capulet mournfully. "She has died the night before her wedding. Death is now my son-in-law. Death is my heir."

Paris was beside himself. He could not believe that this had happened to him. He felt cheated. He had been cheated out of this beautiful wife who was to have been his. "I've waited so long for this morning. Finally it is here. But do I get a bride, my wife, my Juliet? No, I get only death!" With those words, Paris broke down and cried at the foot of his bride's bed.

Everyone in the room was wailing loudly as if their hearts had been broken. Everyone, that is, except for Friar Lawrence, who was suspiciously quiet. He tried to comfort them by saying that Juliet had been taken to heaven. He begged them to dry their tears and remember that Juliet was being well cared for now.

After a long period of time, Lord Capulet composed himself. He slowly began to give directions for turning the wedding celebration into the funeral for his daughter. With heavy hearts, the group began to make its way to the church for Juliet's funeral. Juliet was taken to the Capulet tomb where she was put on a cement block next to her cousin Tybalt. The sorrowful group of mourners left their beautiful Juliet in that cold and dreary tomb. They returned to the Capulet house to continue mourning. The misery in that house was great.

Part V

In Mantua, Romeo had just woken up from a deep
sleep. He had a strange dream that night. He had
dreamt that Juliet had come and found him dead.
When she kissed him, her kisses revived him and he
became an emperor. Romeo thought that this dream
proved the strength of the love he shared with his wife.

These thoughts were interrupted by Romeo's
servant, Balthasar. He had come from Verona with bad
news. When he told Romeo of Juliet's death, the young
man was beside himself with grief. He was devastated.
With his beloved Juliet gone, his thoughts were fixated
on his own death. He wanted to join her in death if he
could not be with her in life. Balthasar was fearful that
Romeo would do something rash. He begged him not to
do something he would regret, but Romeo would not
listen. He told Balthasar to come back in an hour with
horses. They would ride back to Verona together. Romeo
then set about making another plan.

Romeo headed down the street to a shop near his
apartment. He remembered that a poor druggist owned
that shop. He asked the druggist to sell him a poison
that was often used for suicide in those days. At first the
druggist refused to sell the poison to Romeo. "It is
against the law in Mantua to sell that poison. The
punishment is death," said the druggist.

"Please, sir, no one will ever know where I got it. You
look as if you could use some extra money. Are you not

poor? Let me pay you well for this drug. Would forty ducats be sufficient for your trouble?" asked Romeo. He put the money in front of the druggist.

The druggist could not resist. He took the money quickly. In a couple of minutes he was back with the drug. He handed it to Romeo, saying, "This is enough to kill twenty men."

While Romeo was on his way back to Verona, Friar Lawrence was gradually discovering the dreadful events surrounding his plan. He had no idea that Balthasar had ridden to Mantua to tell Romeo of Juliet's death. He had sent Friar John to explain the full details of his plan for the lovers. Much to Friar Lawrence's horror, the letter had never been delivered. Friar John explained that there had been a quarantine in Mantua because of an outbreak of a disease in that city. No one was allowed to go into the area of the city where Romeo lived. Friar John had been unable to find any messenger who would deliver the letter.

Friar Lawrence started to panic. He decided to go to the Capulet tomb to watch over Juliet. "Please, Father John, find me a crowbar and bring it quickly," said Friar Lawrence. Father John left immediately to look for one.

By this time, Romeo and Balthasar had already arrived at the Capulet tomb. Romeo told his servant to leave him there and not to interfere with anything he was doing. These words upset Balthasar so he pretended to go. But he really hid behind a large rock. He was worried about what Romeo might do.

Romeo was surprised to find another man there. It was Count Paris, who was throwing flowers over the door of the tomb. He was shocked and angered to see Romeo at the Capulet tomb. Paris knew that Romeo had killed Tybalt and had been banished. He also knew that Juliet had deeply mourned the loss of her cousin. Paris felt that Juliet's grief was the cause of her death. He blamed Romeo for indirectly killing Juliet. Paris thought that Romeo had come to the tomb to desecrate the bodies there. Perhaps he thought that Romeo was going to steal the burial clothes or jewelry. He became angrier. Paris challenged Romeo to a fight.

Romeo didn't want to fight with anyone. He wanted to get into the tomb so that he could kill himself as soon as possible. He wanted to be with his beloved wife any way that he could. Romeo begged Paris to get out of his way, but he wouldn't. Romeo had no choice but to fight with him. The struggle was very brief. Unfortunately, the one who wanted to die was the one who lived. Paris was killed by a single thrust of Romeo's sword.

"Please, have mercy on me. Open the tomb and lay me with Juliet," said Paris as he died in front of the tomb.

These words startled Romeo. "I must be losing my mind," he said to himself. "Why would Paris want to be buried with Juliet?" Then he started to remember. Balthasar had said something about Paris and Juliet's marrying, but Romeo had not been listening well. He had heard those words as if he were dreaming. At the time, all Romeo could think about was Juliet's death. Was he going mad? He didn't know how Paris was involved in this situation, but he decided to honor his last request.

Romeo carefully pried open the door and dragged Paris into the tomb. As the door opened wider, he saw his beautiful Juliet. She was lying on a long slab of cement. He went to her and looked closely. Romeo could not believe that she looked so beautiful in death. "Death may have taken away your breath, but it has had no effect on your beauty," he whispered lovingly to her. "Your lips and cheeks are blushed with crimson. You have not been dead long enough to show the signs."

At that point Romeo noticed Tybalt lying on the cement slab next to Juliet. He was very upset at the sight. Tybalt was still bloody from the sword fight that killed him. Romeo again felt remorse that he had killed Tybalt even though he had tried to avoid the fight. "Forgive me, cousin," he said to Tybalt. He looked about in despair. Death all around urged him to hurry with his act. Romeo gave Juliet one long last kiss. He drank the poison. His last words were then spoken, "With a kiss I die!" He kissed Juliet one last time and then fell into death.

Friar Lawrence had just entered the Capulet tomb. He was horrified to see Paris lying in a pool of blood and Romeo slumped over Juliet. Juliet had begun to awaken. "Friar, where is my Romeo?" she asked.

"Juliet," he answered, "things did not work out as we planned. Your husband lies dead before you and Paris is dead, too. Hurry, I want to get you out of here before someone comes. I think I hear a noise outside."

"No, Friar, I'm not going anywhere," answered Juliet.

Friar Lawrence quickly left Juliet to check the entry way of the tomb. He was frightened.

Juliet had just seen the bottle of poison that Romeo had taken. "He has drunk it all and left not a drop to help me out of my misery. Maybe there is enough poison left on Romeo's lips to help me die," said Juliet. She kissed her husband's lips. "Your lips are still warm," she said. Juliet realized that she was minutes too late in her waking. She could have stopped Romeo from taking the poison if she had awakened earlier.

Juliet heard the sounds of the night watchmen coming toward the tomb. "I had better do this quickly," she said as she took Romeo's knife from his belt. With a quick motion, she put the knife into her heart and then fell on Romeo. In death, the two bodies were intertwined. It appeared that they died in a loving embrace.

The night watchmen found the tomb in this state. They quickly called the Prince. They also called the Capulet family and the Montague family. The Friar was brought back to the scene. His head drooped with sorrow and shame. Balthasar came out from his hiding place. When all of these people had arrived, the Prince demanded an explanation. The Capulets and Lord Montague had none to offer. Montague was in a state of shock to see his son dead before him. He had lost his wife that very night. She had died of sorrow over Romeo's exile.

Friar Lawrence stepped forward. He told the Prince, "I am the person who can tell you the story. I am afraid that I bear much of the blame for what has happened."

"Then tell us what you know," ordered the Prince.

The Friar began to tell the story of Romeo and Juliet's romance and how he had married them in secret. As he told his story, the parents of the couple began to feel renewed anguish. The Friar related Juliet's fear of telling her parents the truth. And the pain she suffered when her parents made another match for her. He told them of Juliet's desire to kill herself rather than follow through with the second marriage. At this point in the story, tears began slowly falling down Lord Capulet's face. He must surely have been thinking of the anger he had shown his daughter. Perhaps he was thinking about the unkind things he had said to her.

The Friar also explained his plan with the drug. He told the story truthfully. He did not try to make himself less guilty. Then he explained how everything had gone wrong. Romeo had never gotten the letter telling him of the plan. Instead Romeo received only the news of his wife's death. Wanting to be near her in death, he had quickly ridden back to Verona.

The Friar told the Prince that he did not know how Romeo or Paris had died. He had found them dead in the tomb just as Juliet was waking up. The Friar had pleaded with her to leave the tomb. He heard a noise and went to investigate. When he left, she apparently had taken Romeo's knife from his belt and killed herself. He ended his story by saying, "This is all I know. And I would gladly give up my life for my part in this tragedy, Prince." He hung his head in grief. The Friar would never have imagined that the love of this young couple could end so tragically.

"But what happened to Paris and Romeo?" asked the Prince. "Is Romeo's servant anywhere around here?"

Balthasar stepped forward. "I can tell you the rest of the story, Prince," said the servant. He told of bringing the letter to Romeo. He explained how Romeo had taken the news of Juliet's death with such grief that Balthasar feared for his master's life. He told how Romeo had come upon Paris at the tomb. The servant described the fight and Paris's death. He then said that Romeo had written a letter to his father. He gave the letter to the Prince.

The Prince read the letter as all eyes were on him. "The letter confirms the Friar's story. In it Romeo tells his father that he has bought poison from a druggist and that he plans to drink it. He wanted to die next to Juliet in the Capulet tomb."

The Prince slowly folded the letter and then looked up at the families. In a low voice he began to speak. "Capulet and Montague, do you understand what your hate has done to those you loved? Fate has found a way to kill your children through their love. I am at fault here, too. I ignored your feud. And now I have lost more men than I can count. We are all punished."

Capulet turned to Montague. He stretched his hand

52

out to him. "Brother Montague, please give me your hand. For my daughter's sake, let our families be joined. This is all I ask."

"I can give you more than just my hand," answered Montague. "I am going to build a gold statue of your daughter. For as long as the city of Verona stands, I want everyone to know that there could never be one more faithful and true than Juliet."

"And I will build another of Romeo to stand by his wife," answered Capulet. "These statues are small sacrifices considering the losses we have suffered through our fighting."

The Prince looked around at the sorrowful people gathered there in the morning's light. "It is time to close the tomb. Go home now, everyone," he said. "The sun will not be coming out today. It will be gloomy all day long to remind us of our sadness and loss. For never was a story of more woe than this of Juliet and her Romeo."

ROMEO &
JULIET

THE PLAY

Cast of Characters

Capulet Family and Friends
JULIET
LADY CAPULET, *Juliet's mother*
LORD CAPULET, *Juliet's father*
TYBALT, *Juliet's cousin*
PETRUCHIO, *Tybalt's friend*
NANNY, *Juliet's nanny*
SAMSON, *servant*
GREGORY, *servant*
COUNT PARIS, *Juliet's fiance*
COUNT PARIS' SERVANT
CAPULET SERVANT

Montague Family and Friends
ROMEO
LORD MONTAGUE, *Romeo's father*
LADY MONTAGUE, *Romeo's mother*
BENVOLIO, *Romeo's cousin*
MERCUTIO, *Romeo's friend*
BALTHASAR, *servant*
ABRAHAM, *servant*

Other Players
PRINCE OF VERONA, FRIAR LAWRENCE, SERVANTS,
MUSICIANS, FRIAR JOHN, DRUGGIST, POLICE OFFICER,
CHIEF NIGHT WATCHMAN, SECOND NIGHT WATCHMAN,
THIRD NIGHT WATCHMAN, CROWD

Part I

Setting: A street in Verona.

(Samson and Gregory, servants from the Capulet household, enter.)

SAMSON: It's good we have our swords with us just in case we run into someone from the Montague house.

GREGORY: Yes, our masters' quarrels are our quarrels.

SAMSON: You're right. It's all the same.

(Abraham and another servant from the Montague house enter.)

GREGORY: Draw your sword. Here come two men from the house of Montague!

SAMSON: I have my sword ready. Go ahead and pick a fight. I'll back you up.

GREGORY: How will you back me up? By turning your back and running away?

SAMSON: Don't be afraid. I'll be right behind you.

GREGORY: All right. I'll make a face at them as they pass by. We'll see if they do anything about it.

SAMSON: I'll bite my thumb at them. It will be a disgrace to them if they don't do anything about that! *(He makes the obscene gesture.)*

ABRAHAM: Did you do what I think you did, sir?

SAMSON: I bit my thumb, but I didn't mean it for you.

ABRAHAM: What do you mean? You looked straight into my eyes as you bit your thumb.

SAMSON: That's true, but as I said, it was not for you. Now what are you going to do about it?

ABRAHAM: If you're looking for a fight, you're going to get one.

(Swords are drawn by all four men. They begin fighting. Benvolio enters.)

BENVOLIO: Break it up, you fools. You don't know what you're doing!

(Tybalt enters.)

TYBALT: *(Drawing his sword.)* Get ready to die, Benvolio!

BENVOLIO: Tybalt, get hold of yourself. Can't you see that I'm just trying to stop this fight? I want peace. Put your sword away or use it to help me stop this fight.

TYBALT: What makes you think I want peace? I hate that word as much as I hate hell and all of the Montagues, including you. Come on, you coward. Fight like a man!

(Benvolio and Tybalt start to fight. A crowd begins to gather.)

CROWD: Down with the Capulets! Down with the Montagues!

(Lady and Lord Capulet enter.)

CAPULET: What's going on here? Give me my sword.

LADY CAPULET: You old fool. You have more use for a crutch than a sword.

(Lady and Lord Montague enter.)

CAPULET: I need my sword now! Don't you see old Montague will kill me if I can't defend myself?

MONTAGUE: There's my worst enemy, Capulet! Let me at him!

60

(His wife holds him back.)

LADY MONTAGUE: Don't you move one foot to try to get involved in this fight.

(The Prince of Verona enters.)

PRINCE: Listen to me, all of you! You are not men. You are animals! Your anger will not be satisfied until you kill your own neighbors. Throw down those bloody weapons this instant! *(All throw down their swords.)* Listen to me and listen well. I have caught you fighting in the streets three times now. Three times you have disturbed the peace of Verona. Three times you have endangered the lives of our citizens. You don't care about anything except your own battle. You Montagues and Capulets are hateful people. Your fight is so old. You don't even know what you are fighting about. We are all sick of your hatred! If you ever disturb the peaceful streets of Verona again, you will pay for it with your lives! Do you understand? Everyone get out of here NOW!

(All exit except the Montagues and Benvolio.)

MONTAGUE: Who started this fight? Tell me, nephew, were you here when it started?

BENVOLIO: Your servants and servants from the Capulet household were fighting. I tried to separate the men when that hothead Tybalt showed up with a ready sword. He started screaming and swinging his sword in the air. Finally the Prince came and stopped the whole thing.

LADY MONTAGUE: Where is Romeo? Have you seen him today? I'm glad he wasn't involved in this fight.

BENVOLIO: Very early this morning I got up because I couldn't sleep. I decided to take a walk outside the city. I was surprised to see Romeo sitting under a grove of sycamore trees on the west side of Verona. When I started walking toward him, he got up and went in the other direction. I figured that he just wanted to be by himself.

MONTAGUE: He often goes to the woods before the sun comes up. He just sits there in the dark and cries. When the sun comes up, he heads home to lock himself up in his room with his curtains drawn. His moods are not a good thing. I'm very worried about him.

BENVOLIO: Uncle, do you know why he's so unhappy?

MONTAGUE: I don't know. He won't tell me.

BENVOLIO: Have you tried to figure out what is bothering him?

MONTAGUE: I have tried and many of his friends have tried. But he keeps to himself. He won't share his feelings with anyone. If he keeps this up he's going to make himself sick. It's not right to stay locked away in the dark. I wish we could figure out what was troubling him so we could help him.

(Romeo enters.)

BENVOLIO: Here he comes now. If you leave me alone with him, I'll try to find out what's the matter.

MONTAGUE: I would be so happy if you could. Come on, dear, let's leave.

(Lord and Lady Montague exit.)

BENVOLIO: Good morning, cousin.

ROMEO: Is it morning?

BENVOLIO: It's just nine o'clock.

ROMEO: Time goes slowly when you're sad. Was that my father who just left quickly?

BENVOLIO: It was. Why are you so sad?

ROMEO: Because I don't have something that would make me glad.

BENVOLIO: Are you in love?

ROMEO: Out.

BENVOLIO: Of love?

ROMEO: Out of favor with the one I love.

BENVOLIO: Tell me who you love.

ROMEO: I love a woman.

BENVOLIO: I figured out that much.

ROMEO: That was a good guess. She is beautiful, but she doesn't love me. I feel so miserable, I wish I were dead. She has sworn she will not be hit with Cupid's arrow. She wants to die as pure as she was born. What a waste!

BENVOLIO: She never plans to fall in love and marry?

ROMEO: No, she wants none of that. She's too wise, too beautiful.

BENVOLIO: Listen to me, forget about her!

ROMEO: It would be easier to forget to think.

BENVOLIO: You can forget her by giving yourself the freedom to look at other beautiful women.

ROMEO: No one is more beautiful than she. You don't understand. You can't teach me how to forget beauty such as hers.

BENVOLIO: I'll bet I can.

(A servant enters.)

SERVANT: Excuse me, gentlemen. Can either of you read?

ROMEO: Of course, man.

SERVANT: Thank God. *(He hands Romeo a paper.)*

ROMEO: *(Reads.)*
'Signore Martino and his wife and daughters,
Count Anselme and his beautiful sisters,
The lady widow of Vitruvio,
Signore Placentio and his lovely nieces,
Mercutio and his brother Valentine,
My Uncle Capulet, his wife and daughters,
My fair Rosaline and Livia,
Signore Valentino and his cousin Tybalt,
Lucius, and the lively Helena.'

What is this about? Where are these people being invited?

SERVANT: To supper at our house.

ROMEO: Whose house?

SERVANT: My master's.

ROMEO: Of course, I should have asked you that before.

SERVANT: My master is the great, rich Capulet. As long as you are not a Montague, come and join us for a glass of wine. Goodbye! *(Exits.)*

BENVOLIO: Here's a challenge for you. At this dinner party, with many of the beauties of Verona, will be Rosaline, your beloved. Let's go to the party. Compare Rosaline's face to that of the other women, and you will think she looks like a crow.

ROMEO: Don't say that about my beloved. Since the world began there has never been one as pretty as she. You should be burned at the stake for saying such lies.

BENVOLIO: You think she's the most beautiful because you have never compared her to other women. I'll show you women at this party who will put your belief to the true test.

ROMEO: I'll go along, not to look at other women,

but just for the chance to see her.

(Romeo and Benvolio exit.)

Setting: A room at the Capulet house.

(Lady Capulet and Nanny enter.)

LADY CAPULET: Nanny, where is my daughter? Call her for me.

NANNY: I called her. Where is that girl? Juliet!

(Juliet enters.)

JULIET: Who is calling me?

NANNY: Your mother.

JULIET: Here I am, Mother. What do you want?

LADY CAPULET: I have something I want to talk to you about. Nanny, leave us alone. I need to talk to my daughter in private. Nanny, come back again. I just remembered, I need you to hear this. You have known my daughter since she was very young.

NANNY: Yes, I can tell her age to the hour.

LADY CAPULET: She's not quite fourteen.

NANNY: I'll bet you fourteen of my teeth. Oh, wait, I only have four left in my mouth. But I'll bet all of them that she's not yet fourteen. How long is it until August first?

LADY CAPULET: About two weeks and a few days.

NANNY: On the night before August first, she'll turn fourteen. I remember because it is eleven years since the earthquake and that's the time you and your husband were in Mantua. She was the prettiest baby I ever saw. If I could only live to see her married, I'd die happy.

LADY CAPULET: Marriage is exactly what I want to talk to you about. Juliet, my daughter, would you like to be married?

JULIET: It is an honor that I would not dream of.

65

NANNY: Isn't she a wise young lady.

LADY CAPULET: Well, I want you to think about it now. There are many married girls in Verona your age. Some already have children. Why, when I was your age, I had already given birth to you. I'll come right to the point. That very eligible bachelor, Paris, would like to marry you.

NANNY: Now he is a catch! What a fine young man he is.

LADY CAPULET: What do you think, dear? Do you think that you could love this man as your husband? He'll be at the party tonight. Take a close look at him. Read him like you would a book. Study him as if you were getting ready to take a test. Make a task out of staring at him to see what you can learn of him. You don't have to show him that you're looking at him.

NANNY: Some men can grow on you.

LADY CAPULET: Juliet, do you think you can love this man?

JULIET: I don't know, Mother. I could certainly meet him and tell you what I think.

(Servant enters.)

SERVANT: Madam, the guests have arrived. Everyone is asking for you and Juliet. The rest of the servants are cursing Nanny because she isn't helping. I was asked to come and get you.

LADY CAPULET: We're coming. Juliet, the Count is here.

(Lady Capulet, Juliet, and Nanny exit.)

Setting: A street in Verona.

(Romeo, Mercutio, and Benvolio, enter with masks.)

ROMEO: Should we make some kind of excuse for

wearing masks to the party?

BENVOLIO: What can we say? It's not any special event that calls for a mask. Let them think what they will. We'll be gone soon so it doesn't really matter.

ROMEO: Let me carry the torch. Since I am feeling sad, I'll carry the light.

MERCUTIO: No, we want you to be dancing.

ROMEO: Not me. I am too sad to dance. My unhappiness weighs me down like lead. You dance.

MERCUTIO: You are the one who is in love. You should be walking on air.

ROMEO: Is that how love is supposed to make you feel? I feel as if I have been stabbed with cupid's arrow. All I feel is pain.

MERCUTIO: If you feel like that, you have to fight back. If love stabs you with a knife, get a knife and stab it back. Tonight our faces are hidden so we may do as we like!

BENVOLIO: Come on. Let's knock and get in. As soon as we get in, it's every man for himself!

MERCUTIO: Let's go. We're wasting the evening.

ROMEO: I'm afraid. I have a strong feeling that something terrible is going to come of this day. Something will happen tonight that will bring about my death. Yet I feel I have no choice but to go forward. Let's go, gentlemen. Lead the way.

Setting: A hall in the Capulet house.

(Romeo, Mercutio, and Benvolio enter the party.)

CAPULET: Welcome, gentlemen. There are many women who will dance with you. Why, I remember when I was a young man, I used to wear a mask to parties. I've whispered my share of stories to beautiful women while wearing a mask. Those days are gone. You are welcome here. Musicians, begin your playing. Clear the room and quench the fire. The room is too hot for dancing. These masqueraders have added fun to the party.

ROMEO: *(To a servant.)* Who is that lady with that lucky man over there?

SERVANT: I don't know, sir.

ROMEO: She is so beautiful. Her beauty is brighter than the torches we carry. She looks like a dove among crows. She's too gorgeous for this earth. If I ever thought I was in love before, I was not. I have never seen beauty until tonight.

(Tybalt and a servant enter.)

TYBALT: I hear the voice of a Montague! Get me my sword, boy. How dare he come to our party with a mask? He is here to make fun of our family. I will kill him as he stands.

CAPULET: Tybalt, what's the matter with you?

TYBALT: Uncle, there is a Montague here. Our enemy has come to ruin your party!

CAPULET: Is it young Romeo?

TYBALT: Yes, it is that villain, Romeo!

CAPULET: Tybalt, let him alone. He is behaving like a gentleman. And the truth is, he is a well-respected young man of Verona. I will not have him treated poorly in my house. Not for all the money in town. Be patient and ignore him. It is my will. You shall respect it. Stop that scowling and frowning. You are the one who's going to ruin the party.

TYBALT: I cannot stand for a villain to be a guest in this house.

CAPULET: You will stand for it. I am the master in my house. Do not start a fight in my home to show that you are a big man.

TYBALT: But, Uncle, it's such a shame . . .

CAPULET: Go now. I don't want to hear any more of this. Be quiet or I'll make you quiet!

TYBALT: *(To himself.)* I have to be patient even though I'm shaking with anger. Later I'll have a chance to get even.

(Tybalt exits. Romeo approaches Juliet for a dance.)

ROMEO: May I touch your hand? If my touch is too rough, could I kiss your hand to make up for it?

JULIET: You may touch my hand, but you have no need to kiss it. Kissing hands leads to kissing lips.

ROMEO: Then let me go straight to the kissing part. *(He kisses her.)*

JULIET: Oh dear, now I've committed a sin.

ROMEO: A sin from my lips? Then let us sin again. *(He kisses her again.)*

NANNY: Madam, your mother wants to speak to you.

(Juliet exits.)

ROMEO: Who is her mother?

NANNY: Her mother is the lady of the house. She is a good woman. Wise and rich. I'm the young lady's nanny. I have taken care of her since she was a child. Anyone who gets Juliet will get a fortune.

ROMEO: Is she a Capulet? Oh, dear, my life's sworn enemy!

BENVOLIO: Let's get out of here now. We've had our fun.

ROMEO: I think we better.

CAPULET: No, gentlemen, don't go. Well, if you must, goodnight. I guess the party is over. Let's go to bed.

(Exit Lord and Lady Capulet. The masqueraders, musicians, and servants slowly start to leave.)

JULIET: Come here, Nanny. Who is that man over there?

NANNY: I don't know.

JULIET: Go find out his name. *(Nanny exits.)* If he's married, I'll kill myself. *(Nanny returns.)*

NANNY: His name is Romeo. He is the only son of your father's worst enemy.

JULIET: My only love born of my only hate!
It's so unfair that I found out too late!
The unexpected birth of love for me
Means I must love a hated enemy!

NANNY: What are you talking about?

JULIET: Oh, nothing. It's just a rhyme I learned from someone I danced with tonight.

NANNY: Come inside. Everyone has gone now.

(Juliet and Nanny exit.)

Part II

Setting: Capulet's orchard.

(Romeo enters. He is watching Juliet, who is on her balcony.)

ROMEO: What light through yonder window breaks! It is the east and Juliet is the sun. She brightens the sky so. The moon looks dull compared to her. She brings so much light that it looks like daylight when it's dark outside. Her eyes are the fairest stars in the sky. See how she leans her cheek upon her hand. I wish I were a glove so that I could touch her face.

JULIET: Oh, my!

ROMEO: Oh, speak again, angel. For you are as glorious as any angel from heaven.

JULIET: *(Not knowing Romeo hears her.)* Oh, Romeo, Romeo, wherefore art thou, Romeo? Give up your name. Or if you will not, be my love, and I will no longer be a Capulet.

ROMEO: Should I listen for more? Or should I let her know I'm here?

JULIET: After all, it is only your name that is my enemy, not you. And what is a name? What's a Montague? It's not your hand, your foot, your face, nor any other part of the man. What's in a name? That which we call a rose by any other name would smell as sweet. My Romeo would still be perfection if he were called by another name. His name is not part of the person he is. Oh, Romeo, if you could only get rid of that name!

ROMEO: I will hold you to your word. I'll get rid of my name. I'll even be baptized with a new name if you love me! I'll never be Romeo again.

JULIET: Who is out there in the night listening to me?

ROMEO: I don't know how to answer your question without using a name which is hated by you, and, therefore, by me. The name is an enemy to you. If I had written the name, I would tear up the paper.

JULIET: Even though you have spoken fewer than a hundred words, I know who you are. Are you not Romeo, and a Montague?

ROMEO: No, not if you dislike those two.

JULIET: How did you get here? These orchard walls are high and hard to climb. If you are found here by my family, it would mean your death.

ROMEO: I flew over the wall on love's wings. Walls cannot hold out love and your family cannot stop me.

JULIET: If they see you, they will murder you.

ROMEO: There's more danger in your eyes than in twenty of their swords.

JULIET: For all the world, I would not have them find you here.

ROMEO: The darkness of night will protect me against your family. But if you love me, I don't care if they find me. I'd rather die by their hatred than live without your love.

JULIET: Who told you how to get here?

ROMEO: Love directed me. By love I would find where you were.

JULIET: It is a good thing it is dark. You can't see me blushing. I cannot deny that you heard me talking about you. Do you love me, too? Wait, don't answer. I know you will say 'yes.' But you might not be honest about it. You might change your mind tomorrow, thinking I was so easily won over by your words. I could play hard to get and be cold and mean to you. I could act as if I don't like you to keep you interested. But the truth is I am too fond of you to do that. And you will find that my feelings for you will be the same tomorrow. Pardon me for being so open with you and telling you how I feel. I am not like this with everyone.

ROMEO: Lady, I swear by the moon above . . .

JULIET: Oh, don't swear by the moon. The orbit of the moon is always changing. Your love might prove to be changing, too.

ROMEO: What shall I swear by?

JULIET: Don't swear at all. Or if you must, swear by your own sweet self whom I adore. Then I'll believe you.

ROMEO: Dear, love . . .

JULIET: Do not swear. I could not find any happiness in this vow of love tonight. I'm afraid that our feelings of love have come too suddenly like lightning. Maybe we will feel differently tomorrow. Let's just see what happens. We'll say goodnight for now. Let's hope that our love is like a rosebud that will bloom into a gorgeous flower when we meet next.

ROMEO: Don't leave me so unfulfilled tonight.

JULIET: What satisfaction can I give you tonight?

ROMEO: Exchange a vow of love with me.

JULIET: I already gave you mine, though I would like to take it back.

ROMEO: Why would you take it back?

JULIET: So I could give it to you again. The more love I give to you, the more I feel filled with love. My love is deep as the ocean. *(A voice calls Juliet.)* Oh, I hear a voice inside. Goodbye, dear love, sweet Montague, be true. Stay here just a little while. I'll return.

(Juliet exits.)

ROMEO: I'm afraid this is all just a dream. It feels too good to be true.

(Juliet returns.)

JULIET: If your love is honorable, then you will marry me. Send me word tomorrow. Tell me where to meet you for the marriage. I will give you all my fortune. I will follow wherever in the world you go.

NANNY: *(Calling from inside.)* Juliet!

JULIET: I'll be right there. But if you are not serious . . .

NANNY: *(Calling from inside.)* Madam!

JULIET: I'll be there in a minute. *(Whispering to Romeo.)* If you are not serious, leave me alone in my misery. Goodnight. A thousand goodnights to you.

ROMEO: And a thousand times will I miss looking at you tonight.

(Romeo starts to exit.)

JULIET: What time will I hear from you tomorrow?

ROMEO: By nine o'clock in the morning.

JULIET: It will feel like twenty years until then. It's almost morning. You should go. But I keep calling you back to me.

ROMEO: And I gladly come.

JULIET: Goodnight, goodnight. Parting is such sweet sorrow that I shall say goodnight till it be morrow.

ROMEO: Sleep in peace. I will go to speak with the Friar about my happiness and get his help.

Setting: Friar Lawrence's room in the monastery.

(Romeo enters.)

ROMEO: Good morning, Father.

FRIAR: Bless you, son. I'm just getting up. It looks as if you haven't been to bed yet. Is that right?

ROMEO: That is true. I had something much better to do than sleep.

FRIAR: Good heavens, were you up all night with Rosaline?

ROMEO: Rosaline? I've forgotten all about her.

FRIAR: Thank goodness, but where were you?

ROMEO: Well, last night I went to a party in the home of my long-time enemy, Capulet. While I was there I fell in love with the beautiful Capulet daughter and she has agreed to marry me. Will you perform the ceremony today?

FRIAR: Holy St. Francis! What a change of heart! Didn't you tell me that Rosaline was the love of your life? How can you change your feelings like that? Young men love with their eyes, not their hearts. Good grief, think of those tears you wasted. All that groaning and wasting away over the love of Rosaline and now you love someone new?!

75

ROMEO: You scolded me often for loving Rosaline.

FRIAR: I didn't call it love. It was infatuation, son.

ROMEO: Don't be mad. I am in love with someone who loves me in return. Please help us.

FRIAR: I'll see what I can do. This new love of yours may help turn both your families' hatred into love.

ROMEO: Let's hurry!

FRIAR: Let's move wisely and slowly. Those who run often stumble and fall.

(Romeo and Friar exit.)

Setting: A street in Verona.

(Benvolio and Mercutio enter.)

MERCUTIO: I wonder where in the devil that Romeo is? Did he even come home last night?

BENVOLIO: Not to his father's house. Did you know that Tybalt sent a letter to Romeo's house? He challenged Romeo to a duel.

MERCUTIO: I can't believe it!

BENVOLIO: Romeo will fight him. I'm sure of that. Here he comes now.

(Romeo enters.)

MERCUTIO: You gave us the slip last night.

ROMEO: Good morning to you. What are you talking about?

MERCUTIO: You really don't know about the slip you gave us?

ROMEO: Forgive me, Mercutio. I had some important business to attend to last night.

MERCUTIO: Why are you in such a good mood today? No more moaning and groaning about lost love?

(Nanny enters.)

NANNY: Gentlemen, can any of you tell me where Romeo is?

ROMEO: I can tell you where he is because I am he.

NANNY: Can I speak privately with you?

ROMEO: Men, leave me alone for a few minutes. I'll follow you to my father's house. We'll all have dinner there shortly.

MERCUTIO: Very well. Goodbye.

NANNY: Sir, my lady has sent me to find you. Let me tell you right now that if you are leading her on, you are dishonorable.

ROMEO: I can assure you that is not the case.

NANNY: Oh, thank goodness. She will be so happy.

ROMEO: Tell her to come to Friar Lawrence's room in the monastery this afternoon where we will be married. Now take this for your trouble. *(He offers her money.)*

NANNY: No, sir. I could not take a penny.

ROMEO: Take the money. I insist. Please give my love to Juliet.

NANNY: *(Taking the money.)* Yes, a thousand times. I'll tell her to be there this afternoon.

(Nanny and Romeo exit.)

Setting: Capulet's orchard.

(Juliet enters.)

JULIET: Oh, I sent Nanny to find Romeo three hours ago. She promised to return in half an hour. What if he did not come to meet her? No, that cannot be. I must remember that Nanny is lame and walks slowly. If only she were young and in love, she would speed everything up and be back here in no time. Why does she have to be so old and slow and heavy?

(Nanny enters.)

Oh, dearest Nanny. What news do you bring? Did you meet him? Why do you look so sad? Is it bad news?

NANNY: Hold on a minute. My bones are aching and I'm tired.

JULIET: I'll trade you my bones for your news. How can it take so long for you to catch your breath? At least, say if it is good news or bad. Tell me that much. Tell me something!

NANNY: Well, I'll say this much. Romeo has the best physical features of any man you could have chosen. What's for lunch?

JULIET: But what about our marriage?

NANNY: Oh, how my head aches. My back aches, too.

JULIET: I'm sorry you're not feeling well. Now please dearest, sweetest Nanny, tell me what my love said to you.

NANNY: Where is your mother?

JULIET: He said, 'where is your mother?'

NANNY: If you are so anxious, get your own messages next time. Do you have permission to go to church today?

JULIET: I have.

NANNY: Then go to Friar Lawrence's monastery. There will be a man who will make you his wife. Now you're blushing. Go to the church. Take a rope ladder with you for Romeo to climb into your room tonight. Now I'm going to get something to eat. You go to the monastery.

JULIET: What good fortune! Thank you, Nanny, goodbye.

(Juliet and Nanny exit.)

Setting: Friar Lawrence's room in the monastery.

(Romeo and Friar Lawrence enter.)

FRIAR: I hope the heavens will smile on this wedding so that we don't face trouble later.

ROMEO: Nothing can happen to make me regret what I'm doing. As long as I can call Juliet mine, I can face anything, even death.

(Juliet enters and embraces Romeo.)

FRIAR: Ah, here is the lovely Juliet.

JULIET: Good evening, Father.

ROMEO: Oh, Juliet, if I could measure my joy at seeing you, it would turn into a beautiful song.

JULIET: My true love for you has grown so that I cannot even tell you half of it.

FRIAR: Come quickly. I cannot leave you two alone until you are joined in holy matrimony.

(Romeo, Juliet, and Friar exit.)

Part III

Setting: A public place in Verona.

(Benvolio and Mercutio enter.)

BENVOLIO: Let's get out of here. This is a hot day. The Capulets are likely to be around here. If we see them, we're sure to get into a fight. This kind of heat puts everyone in a bad mood.

MERCUTIO: You're one to talk about fighting! You are so jumpy and moody. You are just as likely to pick a fight with me as anyone else. You fight with everybody over everything. Didn't you fight with someone for coughing in the street and waking your dog that was lying in the sun?

BENVOLIO: If I were as bad as you say, somebody should take a bet on how long my life will last. Oh, no, here come the Capulets!

MERCUTIO: Who cares?

(Tybalt and Petruchio enter.)

TYBALT: Gentlemen, good day. May I have a word with one of you?

MERCUTIO: You just want a word with one of us? Are you sure you don't want a word and a blow?

TYBALT: If you give me an excuse to strike you, I will.

MERCUTIO: Then you must be looking for a fight. *(He taps his sword.)*

81

BENVOLIO: This is a public place. Either go to a private place and continue this discussion or leave. Everyone is watching us.

MERCUTIO: Eyes were made for looking. Let them look. I'm not moving.

(Romeo enters.)

TYBALT: Here comes my man now.

MERCUTIO: Well, I'll be hanged. Since when did Romeo become your servant?

TYBALT: Romeo, you are a villain!

ROMEO: Tybalt, I have no reason to be angry with you. In fact, I have more reason to love than hate. I see you don't know me. Otherwise you would not greet me as a villain.

TYBALT: Nothing can excuse the injuries you have done to me. Turn and draw your sword!

ROMEO: I have never injured you. Soon you will find out why I love you and the Capulet name as much as I love my own.

MERCUTIO: *(Drawing his sword.)* Romeo, your words are making me sick. What's wrong with you? Tybalt, come fight with me!

TYBALT: What do you want of me?

MERCUTIO: You're the king of cats and I'm going to take one of your nine lives. Draw!

TYBALT: *(Drawing his sword.)* I'm ready for you.

ROMEO: Mercutio, put away your sword. Benvolio, use your sword to stop this fight. This fighting is shameful. The Prince has outlawed this fighting in the streets. Stop this now! *(Romeo rushes between Tybalt and Mercutio. Tybalt thrusts his sword under Romeo's arm into Mercutio. Mercutio falls.)*

PETRUCHIO: Let's get out of here now!

(Tybalt and Petruchio leave.)

MERCUTIO: I am hurt. Get me a doctor.

ROMEO: Is it bad?

MERCUTIO: It's not as deep as a well or as wide as a church door. But it hurts enough. If you are looking for me tomorrow, you'll find me in a grave. Curse on both your houses! Why did you come between us? I was hurt because of you.

ROMEO: I was trying to stop the fight.

MERCUTIO: Get me out of the street and into someone's house.

(Benvolio helps Mercutio to exit.)

ROMEO: My good friend has been injured and may die because of me. I was trying not to fight with Tybalt because he's my cousin now. My sweet Juliet's beauty softened my bravery and made me act like a woman.

(Benvolio returns.)

BENVOLIO: Romeo, brave Mercutio is dead!

ROMEO: What a black day this is!

(Tybalt enters.)

BENVOLIO: Here comes that furious Tybalt again.

ROMEO: Are you returning to the scene of the crime to gloat? Are you glad you won and Mercutio is dead? Take back your accusation of 'villain.' Take it back for Mercutio's soul that is on its way to heaven. Take it back or one of us will join him.

TYBALT: You're a wretched boy. You were his friend here so you should join him there.

ROMEO: Our fight will determine that.

(They fight. Tybalt is wounded. He falls to the ground.)

BENVOLIO: Romeo, run for your life. Tybalt is dead. Don't just stand there. The Prince will sentence you to death if he finds you. Get out of here!

ROMEO: I'm destiny's fool!

BENVOLIO: Why are you staying?!

(Romeo exits. A police officer enters.)

POLICE: Did you see which way Tybalt, the murderer of Mercutio, ran?

BENVOLIO: Tybalt is there on the ground.

(The Prince, the Montagues, and the Capulets enter.)

PRINCE: Where are the men who started this fight?

BENVOLIO: I can tell you everything, noble Prince. Tybalt started the fight by killing Mercutio. Tybalt was then killed by Romeo.

LADY CAPULET: Oh, dear Tybalt, my brother's child! Prince, is it true that Tybalt was killed because he killed a Montague?

PRINCE: Benvolio, who started this fight?

BENVOLIO: Romeo tried to prevent Tybalt from fighting with Mercutio. They were fighting in spite of him. Romeo wanted to keep the peace. He stepped between Tybalt and Mercutio. Then Tybalt put his sword into Mercutio. Tybalt ran away, but he came back looking for Romeo. He wanted to fight him. This time Romeo was ready for the fight because he wanted revenge for Mercutio's death. I tried to stop it, but Tybalt was quickly killed. Romeo then ran away. This is the truth. I swear to you on my life.

LADY CAPULET: This man is a member of the Montague family. His feelings for his family make him a false witness. He's lying. I beg you for justice, Prince. Romeo killed Tybalt. He must not live.

PRINCE: Romeo killed Tybalt. Tybalt killed Mercutio. Who should pay the price for the bloodshed?

MONTAGUE: Not Romeo, Prince. He was Mercutio's friend. He is not at fault for taking the life of Tybalt. The law would have done this had Tybalt lived.

PRINCE: For taking the life of Tybalt, I will exile him. I have told you I will not tolerate this fighting. I'm deaf to any pleading or excuses. Neither tears nor prayers will move me. Save them. Let Romeo leave quickly. If he is found, he will be killed at once.

(Everyone exits.)

Setting: Capulet's orchard.

(Juliet enters.)

JULIET: I wish the night would hurry. I wish Romeo would hurry. I feel as if I have bought a house of love, but I can't take possession yet. I'm like an impatient child who has new clothes but isn't allowed to wear them.

(Nanny enters.)

NANNY: He's dead! He's dead! He's gone. He's killed.

JULIET: Tell me what happened to my Romeo. Was heaven so envious of him that he has been taken before his time?

NANNY: I can hardly believe it. It's too awful to tell.

JULIET: Tell me what happened! Did Romeo take poison and kill himself? I will kill myself, too. Or was he killed? Tell me what happened!

NANNY: I saw the wounds myself. They were deep and bloody. I saw him lying dead in the streets. It was a horrible sight. I almost fainted.

JULIET: Oh my God! My dearest Romeo is dead! My heart will break.

NANNY: Oh, Tybalt. He was my best friend. What a kind and honest gentleman he was. I can't believe that I have lived to see him dead.

JULIET: What has happened that has caused the death of both my husband and cousin?

NANNY: Tybalt is dead and Romeo has been banished from Verona. Romeo killed Tybalt and the Prince exiled him.

JULIET: Romeo killed Tybalt?

NANNY: Yes, it's true.

JULIET: What a terrible chapter of my life this is!

NANNY: This sadness makes me feel old. Where's my mineral water? Shame on Romeo.

JULIET: Hold your tongue!

NANNY: He killed your cousin.

JULIET: I don't care. Would it have been better if my cousin had killed my husband? Tybalt's death is a terrible thing, but the fact that Romeo is banished makes it 10,000 times worse. Where are my mother and father, Nanny?

NANNY: They are mourning over Tybalt's body. Do you want to join them?

JULIET: My tears are reserved for Romeo's exile. I'm destined to die a widow without ever having a wedding night.

NANNY: Go to your room. I'm sure he is hiding with Friar Lawrence. I'll bring him to you tonight. Don't worry.

JULIET: When you find him, give him this wedding ring. Beg him to come and say his last goodbye to me.

(Juliet and Nanny exit.)

Setting: Friar Lawrence's room at the monastery.

(Romeo enters. He is looking out the window. Friar Lawrence enters.)

ROMEO: What have you heard in town?

FRIAR: I'm afraid it is bad news. You have been banished by the Prince.

ROMEO: I would rather be dead than to be sent away from Verona. A sentence of death would be better than exile.

FRIAR: Our law calls for your death for this crime, but the kind Prince has shown mercy on you. Can't you see that?

ROMEO: Juliet lives here in this city. Heaven is where she lives. Everywhere else is hell.

(Nanny enters.)

NANNY: Where is Romeo?

FRIAR: Right now he is drowning in his own tears.

NANNY: Oh my, he's in the same state as Juliet. She just lies on her bed, weeping and crying out. She is beside herself. Stand up, Romeo. For Juliet's sake, stand up and be a man.

ROMEO: How is she? Does she think I'm a murderer? Does she still love me?

NANNY: She says nothing. She cries and cries. She cries for her cousin and then she cries for her husband. Every time she tries to get up, she falls down and begins weeping again.

ROMEO: I have killed her beloved cousin and

caused her much pain. I should just kill myself. It is what I deserve. *(He grabs a knife, but Nanny takes it away.)*

FRIAR: Are you a man? If you are, act like one. For goodness sake, you cry like a woman and you act like an animal. Pull yourself together, boy. You still have many reasons to be happy. The Prince could have sentenced you to death. Instead, he spared your life. You have the love of a beautiful woman. All these things should make you happy. Yet you cry like a child when you should be comforting your wife. Go to her room. Spend what little time you have left with Juliet. In the morning, go to Mantua. When some time has passed, I will talk to the Prince. I'll persuade him to give you a pardon. When he finds out that you and Juliet are married, he'll show you even more mercy. Nanny, go to Juliet and tell her that her husband is on his way.

NANNY: You are such a wise man! I'll go to Juliet now and give her the news. Romeo, here is the wedding ring that Juliet told me to give to you. Come quickly because it's getting late.

(Nanny exits.)

ROMEO: I'm starting to feel better, Father. Maybe things will work out.

FRIAR: Remember, Romeo, you must leave Juliet before the break of day. If you don't, the police will catch you. Leave before it is light out. Take your servant and go to Mantua. I will send messages to you to let you know how things stand. *(The Friar takes Romeo's hand and shakes it.)* Be patient. Things will work out. Goodbye.

(Romeo and Friar Lawrence exit.)

Setting: A room in the Capulet house.

(Count Paris and Lord and Lady Capulet enter.)

CAPULET: Paris, it's very late. Too late for Juliet to come down. I would have been in bed an hour ago if it had not been for your visit. Besides Juliet is not feeling well. She is mourning the loss of her dear cousin, Tybalt.

PARIS: I know. These are sad times.

CAPULET: Paris, I will try to persuade my daughter to marry you. I think she will do as I say. Wife, go to Juliet and tell her that Paris loves her and wants to marry her. Tell her we would like the wedding to be on Thursday. It will be a small wedding. We don't want people to think that we have forgotten about Tybalt. What do you think about Thursday?

PARIS: I only wish that tomorrow was Thursday. The sooner the better!

CAPULET: Then Thursday it will be. Goodnight.

(Count Paris and the Capulets exit.)

Setting: Juliet's chamber.

(Romeo and Juliet enter.)

JULIET: Are you leaving? It is not yet morning. That song you heard was the nightingale. I know the song well. He sits on a tree in the orchard and sings me to sleep each night.

ROMEO: That was the lark. It was the lark telling us that morning has arrived. I must be gone. If I stay I will be discovered. If I am discovered, I will be killed.

JULIET: It cannot be morning yet. There is not

enough light outside to guide you on your way to Mantua.

ROMEO: For you I will stay and be killed then. Let's just stay here together. I want to stay more than I care to go. If my Juliet wills my death, then I welcome it.

JULIET: Go, Romeo. Go now.

ROMEO: *(Looking out the window.)* The lighter it becomes outside, the darker our troubles.

(Nanny enters quickly.)

NANNY: Juliet, your mother is coming to your room. It's morning. Get up.

JULIET: The day is coming in the window. My life is going out that same window.

ROMEO: Farewell, my darling. One kiss and I'll be gone.

JULIET: You must write to me every hour. I will count every minute until we are together.

ROMEO: Farewell. I promise to send my love to you every chance I get.

JULIET: Do you think we will ever see one another again?

ROMEO: I know for sure that we will be together again. Our troubles will fade. There will be sweet times ahead.

JULIET: Oh no, I just had an awful feeling. When I looked down at you, it felt as though I were looking down into a tomb. My eyesight might be failing, but you look so pale.

ROMEO: Trust me, darling love, our sadness makes us both look pale. Goodbye, goodbye.

JULIET: Fortune, please don't be fickle. Send my Romeo back to me.

(Lady Capulet enters.)

LADY CAPULET: Daughter, are you up?

JULIET: Yes, but I am not well.

LADY CAPULET: Are you still mourning the loss of Tybalt? Do you think your tears will wash him from his grave? It's good to show grief. It proves your love, but too much grief is foolish.

JULIET: I can't help myself. I have to cry for the loss I feel.

LADY CAPULET: I know that your loss is made worse by the fact that his murderer still lives. Do not worry, dear. I have a plan. I am going to hire someone to poison Romeo. I have heard he is hiding out in Mantua. He will be dead before you know it. Just like Tybalt.

JULIET: I shall never be satisfied until Romeo is dead.

LADY CAPULET: I'll find a man to do the deed. But now I have good news to tell you.

JULIET: I could use some good news. What is it?

LADY CAPULET: Your father has arranged a special surprise for you to help you over your sadness. You will soon have joy in your life that you had not expected.

JULIET: What do you mean?

LADY CAPULET: This Thursday morning you will be married to Count Paris at St. Peter's Church. What a joyful bride you will be!

JULIET: I will not be a joyful bride. What is the great hurry that I have to marry before I am even courted? Please tell my father that I will not marry yet. When I do, I'd sooner marry Romeo than Paris.

(Capulet and Nanny enter.)

LADY CAPULET: Here is your father now. Tell him yourself.

CAPULET: Wife, have you given Juliet the good news?

LADY CAPULET: Yes, I have, but she said 'no, thank you.'

CAPULET: What?! Did you say that she is NOT counting her blessings that a man such as Paris wants to marry her? Are you telling me that she doesn't appreciate her parents' efforts in finding the best husband in all of Verona? Is this what you are telling me?

JULIET: I do thank you, but I don't love him so I must refuse this offer.

CAPULET: You are an ungrateful daughter. You are a spoiled brat. You should get down on your knees and thank us for arranging such a match. Instead you try to tell me that you will not marry?! My answer to you is that you will be at that church on Thursday if I have to drag you the whole way. You, daughter, are a useless piece of baggage!

LADY CAPULET: Shame on you.

JULIET: Please, Father, listen to me for just a few words.

CAPULET: You will not speak to me, you disobedient child. I am disgusted with you. Don't you dare say another word to me about this. If you are not at that church on Thursday, you are no longer my daughter. Here we thought we were lucky because we had a child. As it turns out, one child is one too much!

NANNY: Sir, you cannot mean that.

CAPULET: Silence. Nobody wants to hear a nanny's opinion about this matter.

NANNY: Sir, could I just say one thing?

CAPULET: No, you may not. Save it for your gossip sessions with your friends.

LADY CAPULET: *(To her husband.)* Calm down. You are too angry.

CAPULET: I have a right to be angry. I have worked hard all of my life to provide for this child. Finally, when I have made her the best match in Verona, she refuses him. And why does this foolish girl refuse him? 'I don't love him. I'm too young. He hasn't courted me.' Well, let me tell you. If you do not marry this man I have chosen for you, you will not live in this house ever again. You will die a beggar in the streets. I will never set eyes on you again.

(Capulet exits.)

JULIET: Mother, please help me. Get him to delay the marriage for a week or maybe a month. Please, Mother.

LADY CAPULET: Don't bother talking to me. I'm not going to say a word to your father. Do as you will. There will be no more discussion.

(Lady Capulet exits.)

JULIET: What am I to do, Nanny? Please tell me what to do.

NANNY: This is the way it is. Romeo is banished. If he comes back, he's going to be killed. I think you should marry Count Paris. He is handsome and rich. Why, Romeo is a dishrag compared to him. I think you'll be happy in this second match. It's better than your first. Even if it weren't, your first is as good as dead. He's of no use to you.

JULIET: Do you really think it's best?

NANNY: Absolutely.

JULIET: *(Slowly speaking.)* Yes, I suppose you are right. Thank you for your good advice and comfort. Please go tell my mother that I have gone to Friar Lawrence to be forgiven for displeasing my father.

NANNY: You have made a wise decision.

(Nanny exits.)

JULIET: What a foolish woman she is! She wants me to disavow my marriage to Romeo. That would be a sin. She praised him many times, but she quickly forgets him and recommends another. I'll go to Friar Lawrence and ask for help. If all else fails, I'll kill myself.

(Juliet exits.)

Part IV

Setting: Friar Lawrence's room in the monastery.

(Friar Lawrence and Paris enter.)

FRIAR LAWRENCE: You want me to perform the wedding on Thursday? That's such short notice.

PARIS: My future father-in-law wants it that soon, and I don't disagree with him.

FRIAR LAWRENCE: You say that you don't even know if Juliet has consented.

PARIS: She has been so sad because of Tybalt's death that I have not been able to properly propose. That's why Lord Capulet wants the wedding to be so soon. He thinks that it will help Juliet get rid of the sorrow she feels.

(Juliet enters.)

PARIS: I am happy to see you, my Juliet and my wife.

JULIET: That might be true when I am your wife, but not today.

PARIS: It will be true next Thursday.

JULIET: What will be, will be.

PARIS: Did you come to make a confession to Friar Lawrence? Be sure to confess your love for me.

JULIET: Friar, do you have time to hear my confession?

FRIAR: Of course, my dear.

PARIS: I will not disturb your confession, but I must have a kiss before I go. *(He quickly kisses Juliet.)* Keep this kiss until Thursday when there will be many more!

(Paris exits.)

JULIET: Oh, Friar, shut the door. When you have done that, come and cry with me. I am past help and hope.

FRIAR: Oh, Juliet, I know all about it.

JULIET: If you can't help me, I have no other choice but to end my life. *(Juliet pulls a knife out of her cloak.)* I have been joined with Romeo in marriage. I must be faithful to him, or I will die.

FRIAR: Stop, Juliet. Please, I have a desperate plan that will save you from this marriage to Paris.

JULIET: Oh, tell me. Tell me quickly. I'll do anything to avoid marrying Paris. I don't care how desperate your plan is.

FRIAR: Listen carefully. On Wednesday night, go to your bedroom without your nanny. Take this drug and drink it all. It will make you appear to be dead. The effects of the drug will last for forty-two hours. Then you will awake as if you have had a pleasant sleep. When Paris comes to take you to church, he will think you are dead. You will be taken to the Capulet tomb where you will wait for Romeo. I will make sure that Romeo knows of the plan. He will be there by your side when you wake up. Romeo and you can then go to Mantua. Juliet, you must be a very brave girl to follow through with this plan.

JULIET: Give me the drug. Don't talk to me about fear. I have no choice.

FRIAR: *(Giving her the bottle.)* Be strong, Juliet.

JULIET: Love will give me the strength I need. Farewell, dear Friar.

(Friar Lawrence and Juliet exit.)

Setting: Juliet's chamber.

(Juliet and Nanny enter. They are carrying clothes.)

JULIET: These are my best clothes. Dear Nanny, tonight I need to be by myself. I have to pray to heaven that I will be forgiven for this sin. You know what I'm talking about.

(Lady Capulet enters.)

LADY CAPULET: Do you need my help?

JULIET: No, Mother, we have everything ready for tomorrow. I'd like to be alone now. Nanny can help you. I'm sure that you have your hands full with the wedding plans.

LADY CAPULET: Goodnight, dear. Get yourself some rest. You will need it.

(Lady Capulet and Nanny exit.)

JULIET: Goodnight. God only knows when we shall meet again. I'm so scared. Maybe I should call them back to comfort me. No, what can they do? I have to act alone. What if this drug doesn't work? Will I be married tomorrow morning? No, this will prevent it. *(Juliet puts a knife down on the bed.)* What if the Friar has given me poison instead of the sleeping drug? He might want me dead. Maybe he's afraid he will get into trouble for marrying Romeo and me. That can't be true. He's a holy man. What if I wake up alone before Romeo gets there? What if I suffocate because I can't breathe in the tomb? Or what if the ghosts of my ancestors come to haunt me?

What if Tybalt comes after me for marrying the man who murdered him? I'm so frightened. Romeo, Romeo, I drink to you. *(She takes the drug and falls into the bed.)*

Setting: Morning – Juliet's chamber.

(Nanny enters.)

NANNY: Juliet, dear, are you still in bed? Come on, sleepy head. *(She draws back the curtains.)* What? Did you dress early this morning and then fall back asleep? It's time to wake up. *(She shakes her. Then puts her face close to Juliet's.)* Oh, no! She's dead! Help! Help! Juliet is dead!

(Lady Capulet enters.)

LADY CAPULET: What are you screaming about? What is going on here?

NANNY: Look for yourself! What a terrible day!

LADY CAPULET: Oh, no! My child, the love of my life. You must be revived or I will die with you. Help, help! Get help!

(Lord Capulet enters.)

CAPULET: Paris is here for Juliet. Bring her downstairs.

NANNY: She's dead! She's dead! What a terrible day!

CAPULET: Let me see her. *(He looks her over carefully. He picks up her hand and holds it.)* You are right. She is cold. Her body is stiff from death. Her lips have no color. It is as if death has come like an early frost to kill the sweetest flower in the field.

NANNY: What a horrible day!

LADY CAPULET: This is dreadful!

CAPULET: I am too sad to speak!

(Friar Lawrence and Paris enter.)

FRIAR LAWRENCE: Is the bride ready to go to the church?

CAPULET: She's ready to go to the church, but she will never come back again. Son, the night before your wedding, death has taken your wife. Death is my son-in-law. My daughter has married death! Death is my heir!

(Paris, Nanny, and Lord and Lady Capulet all cry.)

PARIS: I have waited so long for this morning. Finally it is here. But do I get my bride, my wife, my Juliet? No, I get only death!

LADY CAPULET: This is the most miserable day of my life! I was given only one child, one loving child. Now that child has been snatched away from me by death.

NANNY: This is such a hateful day! I've never seen such a black day. This is too much for me to bear.

CAPULET: My child, my child. My child is dead. All my joy in life will be buried with her.

FRIAR LAWRENCE: There, there, let's not carry on so. Remember, you always shared this child with God. Now she's in heaven and she's better off there. You could not keep death from your child, but heaven will keep her in eternal life. She is high above the clouds now. Dry your tears and prepare the body for burial. Let's bring her to the church and mourn her passing.

CAPULET: Everything prepared for the wedding will now be used for the funeral. No musicians, only church bells. The wedding reception must be changed to a burial feast. The wedding music must now be a funeral dirge. The bridal flowers must be buried with the body.

FRIAR LAWRENCE: Come now, Lord and Lady Capulet. Go with them, Count Paris. Everyone should accompany the corpse to her grave.

(All exit.)

Part V

Setting: A street in Mantua.

(Romeo enters.)

ROMEO: I had a very strange dream. I dreamt that Juliet came and found me dead. She breathed such life into me with her kisses that I became an emperor. My love for her is so great that it gives me wonderful dreams.

(Balthasar, Romeo's servant, enters.)

Do you have news from Verona? Did the Friar send me a letter? How is Juliet? Is my father well? Tell me about Juliet. Nothing can be wrong if she is well.

BALTHASAR: I'm afraid her body has been put to rest in the Capulet tomb. I saw her buried today. I came as quickly to tell you. Please forgive me for bringing you such terrible news.

ROMEO: How can this be? I cannot believe it is true. Get me some ink and paper. Hire some horses. I will leave tonight.

BALTHASAR: Please, sir, be patient. You have a wild look in your eyes. I'm afraid that you're going to do something rash.

ROMEO: Leave me alone and do as I ask. Don't you have any letter from the Friar for me?

BALTHASAR: No, sir.

ROMEO: It doesn't matter. Get going. Hire those horses and I'll be there soon.

(Balthasar exits.)

ROMEO: Juliet, I will lie with you tonight. Let me think how this will be done. I remember an old druggist who appeared to be very poor. He has a shop close by. His shop was over here. Hey, druggist!

(The druggist enters.)

DRUGGIST: Who calls so loudly?

ROMEO: Come here, man. I see you are poor. *(He holds out money to the druggist.)* Here is forty ducats. I need to buy some poison that will quickly put a man to death.

DRUGGIST: I have such a drug, but it is against Mantua law to sell it.

ROMEO: Look at yourself. You are so poor. You're starving to death. The world has not been your friend. Why do you care about the world's laws? There are no laws to help you get rich, only laws to make you poor. Take this money and rid yourself of poverty.

DRUGGIST: I'm breaking the law only because my poverty is forcing me. *(Gives Romeo the poison.)* Put this in any liquid and drink it all. It's enough to kill twenty men.

ROMEO: *(Gives the druggist the money.)* Here is your money. Money is like poison to men's souls. It does more murder in this world than all of your poisons that the law says are illegal. I will not tell anyone what you have done. Goodbye. Buy yourself some food. *(Druggist exits.)* I must go to Juliet's grave and use this poison.

(Romeo exits.)

Setting: Friar Lawrence's room in the monastery.

(Friar John enters.)

FRIAR JOHN: Hello, brother.

(Friar Lawrence enters.)

FRIAR LAWRENCE: Is that you, Friar John? Welcome back from Mantua. What did Romeo say?

FRIAR JOHN: I couldn't get a messenger to deliver your letter. There was a quarantine in Mantua.

FRIAR LAWRENCE: Well, who gave my letter to Romeo?

FRIAR JOHN: No one. I could not get it there. Here it is. *(He hands the letter to Friar Lawrence.)*

FRIAR LAWRENCE: Oh, no, I can't believe this! The contents of that letter were so important. I'm afraid that someone is in danger now. Hurry, Friar John. Get me a crowbar. Bring it to my room!

FRIAR JOHN: Yes, Brother, I'll get one right away.

FRIAR LAWRENCE: I must get to the tomb at once. Juliet will be awake in less than three hours. She will be very upset that Romeo doesn't know what has happened. I'll write to Mantua again. I can keep her here in the monastery until Romeo can come. Oh, poor Juliet, closed in a dead man's tomb!

(Friar Lawrence exits.)

Setting: A churchyard.

(Paris and his servant enter.)

PARIS: Give me your torch, boy. I want you to put out the light and stand guard here. Listen carefully. If you hear anyone, I want you to whistle as a signal. Give me those flowers.

SERVANT: I'm afraid to stand here by myself. It's scary in the cemetery. *(He slowly exits.)*

PARIS: *(Throwing flowers).* My sweet Juliet. These flowers were to be for your bridal bed. I'm going to come here every night to throw flowers on your grave and cry. *(His servant whistles.)* That's the signal!

Somebody must be coming. What cursed feet are coming this way to destroy these moments with my love?

(Romeo and Balthasar enter with a crowbar. Count Paris moves aside.)

ROMEO: Give me the crowbar. Take this letter. Tomorrow morning I want you to deliver this to my father. Whatever you see me do here tonight, stand aside. Do not try to stop me. I am going to die tonight because I must be with my beloved. I came here because I want to see her face one last time. I'm warning you. If you try to stop me, I'll tear you from limb to limb. I'll spread your body parts around the churchyard. Do you understand?

BALTHASAR: I'll leave, sir. I won't bother you.

ROMEO: You have always shown me good friendship. Take this. *(He gives him money.)* Live a prosperous life, my friend. Goodbye.

BALTHASAR: *(Leaving.)* I'll stay here and hide to see what happens. I can't believe he's going to do what he says.

(Balthasar hides as Romeo uses the crowbar to open the tomb.)

ROMEO: I'm forcing these rotten jaws of death open. Soon there will be more death for these jaws to consume!

PARIS: *(Aside.)* That's the voice of that Montague who murdered my love's cousin. It was from her grief that my beautiful Juliet died. He's probably come here to shame the dead bodies in this tomb! I will stop him! *(Drawing his sword.)* Get off this holy soil, Montague! I'm going to take you to the authorities. You must die for your villainous acts!

ROMEO: You're right. I must die and that's why I am here. Leave me alone and let me die in peace. Don't make me commit another sin by hurting you. Get out of here! I don't want to do harm to anyone except myself.

PARIS: I am arresting a felon. Come with me now!

ROMEO: *(Drawing his sword.)* I told you not to provoke me! If a fight is what you want, then you will have it!

(They fight.)

SERVANT: Oh no, my master is fighting. I had better call the police!

(Servant exits. Paris is struck.)

PARIS: Oh, I have been killed! If you have any mercy, open the tomb. Let me lie with Juliet. *(He dies.)*

ROMEO: Who is this man? Is this Count Paris? Did my servant tell me that Juliet was to have married him? I hardly heard him because my thoughts were on Juliet's death. Is it possible that it's true? *(He opens the tomb and drags Paris's body in.)* Here lies my beautiful Juliet. The death that has taken her sweet breath away has had no effect on her beauty. Her cheeks and lips are the color of crimson. The pale flag of death has not yet risen on my love. Is it Tybalt over there under that bloody sheet? What better favor could I do you than to take my own life with the same hand that took yours. Forgive me, cousin. Oh, Juliet, how can it be that you are still so fair? Is it possible that death wants to keep you for his bride? Go away. You cannot have my Juliet. I will stay by her side until the worms have our flesh. Eyes, take your last look. Arms, take your last embrace. And, lips, take your last kiss. *(He kisses Juliet and pours the poison into a cup.)* I drink to my love. *(He drinks the poison.)* The druggist was telling the truth. The poison works swiftly. With this kiss, I will die. *(He kisses Juliet and falls dead on her. Friar Lawrence enters with a crowbar.)*

FRIAR LAWRENCE: I have rushed here as quickly as I could. These old feet have tripped over many graves on the way here. Who's there?

BALTHASAR: A friend.

FRIAR LAWRENCE: Tell me, good friend, whose torch is that in the Capulet tomb?

BALTHASAR: It is my master, Romeo.

FRIAR LAWRENCE: How long has he been there?

BALTHASAR: For a half hour.

FRIAR LAWRENCE: Come with me into the tomb.

BALTHASAR: I don't dare, sir. He's threatened to kill me if I don't stay out of his business.

FRIAR LAWRENCE: Very well, then I'll go alone even though I'm fearful.

BALTHASAR: As I slept under that tree over there, I dreamt that my master and another man fought. In my dream, my master killed the other man.

FRIAR LAWRENCE: *(Seeing the blood and weapons.)* Romeo! Whose blood stains are these? *(He follows the stains into the tomb.)* Romeo and Paris, too. How could this have happened?

(Juliet awakens and sits up.)

JULIET: Friar, where is Romeo? I remember everything that happened. Here I am, but where is Romeo?

FRIAR LAWRENCE: I hear a noise, Juliet. Come with me. Things did not work out as we planned. Your husband lies dead before you. Paris is dead, too. Come with me. I'll take you to a nunnery. Don't ask any more questions. I don't dare stay any longer.

JULIET: Then go and get out of here. I'm not leaving. What is this? A cup in my love's hand. I see that he has poisoned himself. He has drunk all of the poison and left not a drop to help me out of my misery. Maybe there is enough poison left on Romeo's lips to help me die. *(She kisses Romeo's lips.)* Your lips are still warm. I hear a noise. I had better do this quickly. *(She takes Romeo's dagger.)* Oh, dagger, bring me a happy death. *(She stabs herself and falls dead on Romeo.)*

(Paris' servant and watchmen enter.)

CHIEF WATCHMAN: What a terrible sight! Count Paris has been killed. Juliet is bleeding and warm yet she has been buried for two days now. Go get the Prince. Get the Montagues and Capulets! Hurry now. Search the rest of the churchyard. Maybe someone saw what happened here.

(Two more watchmen enter with Balthasar and the Friar.)

2ND WATCHMAN: Here's Romeo's servant. I found him hiding in the cemetery grounds.

3RD WATCHMAN: I found the Friar walking out of the churchyard with a shovel and crowbar. He's trembling like a leaf and crying about something.

CHIEF WATCHMAN: That sounds suspicious. Hold him here.

(The Prince, Lord and Lady Capulet, and others enter.)

PRINCE: Why are we awakened at the crack of dawn to come down here?

CAPULET: Why are all these people running and screaming in the streets?

107

LADY CAPULET: We heard people cry out 'Romeo.' Some were saying 'Juliet.' Others were saying 'Paris.' They were all running toward our tomb in the churchyard.

PRINCE: What is going on here?

CHIEF WATCHMAN: Prince, we have discovered the slain body of Count Paris. We have also found Romeo's body. And a very odd thing . . . Juliet's body was found warm and bleeding as if she recently died.

PRINCE: Find out how this all happened

CHIEF WATCHMAN: Friar Lawrence was also found here with the tools to open the tomb.

CAPULET: Oh my heaven! Wife, look at our daughter's blood all over the place. The knife that should have been reserved for Montague's back has mistakenly ended up in our daughter's chest.

LADY CAPULET: All this death reminds me that I will soon be in this very tomb.

(Montague enters.)

PRINCE: Montague, you have been given an early call this morning to see your son take an early fall.

MONTAGUE: My wife died of grief last night because of her son's exile. What further suffering can I be in for?

PRINCE: Look and see for yourself.

MONTAGUE: *(Seeing his son's body.)* How can this be?

PRINCE: Silence! Let's listen to the explanations of those who were in the churchyard.

FRIAR LAWRENCE: I will explain everything.

PRINCE: Then tell us what you know.

FRIAR LAWRENCE: I will be brief. Romeo and Juliet were husband and wife. I married them the same day that Tybalt was killed. Juliet

108

was beside herself with grief because her new husband had been exiled. Her parents were forcing her to marry Count Paris. She came to me for help. Juliet told me that she would kill herself rather than marry another. I gave her a sleeping drug that made her appear to be dead. I wrote to Romeo and told him to come get Juliet from the tomb when she wakened. He never got the letter. So I came here to the tomb to be with Juliet when she woke up. I found both Romeo and Paris dead. Juliet woke up. I begged her to come with me. Then a noise scared me so I ran out of the tomb. She would not go with me. She stayed behind to kill herself with the knife. That is all I know. Juliet's nanny knows the story, too. If I am at fault for this tragedy, then take my life.

PRINCE: We have always known you to be a holy man, Friar Lawrence. Where is Romeo's servant? What can he add to the story?

BALTHASAR: I brought the news of Juliet's death to Romeo in Mantua. He insisted on coming back to Verona to this tomb. He gave me this letter to give to his father. When we got to the tomb, he told me that he would kill me if I didn't leave him alone.

PRINCE: Let me see the letter. *(He takes the letter from Balthasar.)* Where is the Count's servant who called the night watchmen? What brought your master here, boy?

SERVANT: He came to bring flowers to Juliet's grave. He told me to keep out of his way. Then I saw another man come to the tomb. This man and my master started to fight. My master drew his sword first. It was then that I ran to call the night watchmen.

PRINCE: This letter verifies the Friar's story. It

tells of Romeo and Juliet's love, and how Romeo bought poison from a poor druggist. He then came to the vault to die with his wife. Capulet and Montague, do you understand what your hatred has done to those you love? Fate has found a way to kill your children through their love. I am at fault here, too. I ignored your feud. Now I have lost more men than I can count. We are all punished.

CAPULET: Brother Montague, please give me your hand. For my daughter's sake, let our families be joined. That is all I can ask.

MONTAGUE: I can give you more than just my hand. I am going to build a gold statue of your daughter. For as long as Verona stands, I want everyone to know that there could never be one more faithful and true than Juliet.

CAPULET: And I will build another of Romeo to stand by his wife. These statues are small sacrifices considering the losses we have suffered through our fighting.

PRINCE: Go home now, everyone. The sun will not be coming out today. It will be a gloomy day to remind us of our sadness and loss. For never was a story of more woe than this of Juliet and her Romeo.

(The tomb is closed. All exit.)

THE GLOBE THEATER

The Globe Theater may well be the most famous theater in the world, for it was here that Shakespeare and other literary giants of his day produced their plays and other dramatic works.

Shakespeare and several other well-known actors needed a place to perform and so they pooled their funds and designed and built the Globe in 1599. Since they were theatrical professionals in every sense of the word, the building fit their needs perfectly. The Globe was octagonally-shaped with a roofless inner pit into which the stage projected. Three galleries (balconies) rose one above the other, the topmost of which had a thatched roof. One day, in order to provide reality in a production of Shakespeare's *King Henry the Eighth*, a cannon was discharged. Unfortunately, this piece of stagecraft set fire to the thatched roof, and the entire building burned. It was rebuilt the following year but was torn down by the Puritans 30 years later who needed the space for houses.

Today in London work is underway to build a new Globe Theater using only materials that would have been found in the original Globe – a perfect setting to enjoy Shakespeare's genius.

About the Editors

Peggy L. Anderson, PhD, is a professor and Special Education Program Coordinator at Metropolitan State College of Denver. She has taught students with learning disabilities at the elementary and middle school levels in South Carolina and Florida. Her master's degree is from the Citadel and her doctorate is from the University of Denver. She completed her postdoctoral work with the Department of Pediatrics at Johns Hopkins University. Her research interests have focused on language-learning disabilities, dyslexia, and inclusion issues.

Judith D. Anderson, JD, is a trial attorney in southern California, specializing in the defense of school districts. She has taught Shakespeare to high school students in the United States and the United Kingdom for ten years. As a Fullbright Scholar, she travelled extensively in the British Isles, and met with the Queen Mother of England. She received her bachelor's degree at Flagler College and her law degree at Southwestern University School of Law.